Four on a Flatcar

by G.D. Jacobson

1995
Everett, Washington
The PRINT SHOP at the BEND in the RIVER

Author's Acknowledgment:
I would like to thank the following talented
people for their help in making this book
possible: Mike Henderson for his fine editing;
Elizabeth Webber for her artistry, skill, and
grace; Steve Heinzen for putting it all together
and guiding me through the publishing process.

FOUR ON A FLATCAR

This edition was designed, printed, and bound
by Lowell Printing & Publishing
The Print Shop at the Bend in the River
5409 South Second Avenue
Everett, WA 98203
206-339-3718
LP&P #035

ISBN 1-881147-18-5

*Dedicated to the memory
of Duane Jacobson*

Chapter 1

The summer of 1948, when I was 17 and my brother Duane was 15, and when we were about to embark unknowingly on our greatest adventure, was in many larger ways a crossroads of the American adventure. The old era had all but ended with the war. It was a time of rapid transition, with the death of old heroes such as Babe Ruth that summer coming just as America's new popular wonder -- television -- was being born. The America of the old, vanishing era was one where the railroads still commanded travel and commerce, and where a young man's innocence was as vast as the dreams we could summon on a lazy summer afternoon.

The new era was one of bustling activity, with the war veterans settling into the emerging suburbs and claiming every available job of a post-war economy that was rebuilding the war-torn world. Duane and I were still too young to sense the rush of vitality that was energizing the new America. What we knew for sure though was that we had missed the century's main adventure. Too young for World War II (though we kept track of the action through radio and newsreel accounts), our context for adventure was limited to a neighborhood where the boundaries didn't extend much beyond North Seattle. We lived in the home our dad had built a few blocks above Lake City Way, which had been the main route to the road houses and resorts strung along toward Bothell in the early years of the century. Our main rush was afforded from sneaking onto the municipal golf courses and playing a few free holes on days that we were hunting and selling golf balls for spending money.-- that or hanging out and harmonizing with neighborhood friends.

Needless to say, Duane and I and our closest friends always were pretty near broke. Then again, it didn't take much to satisfy a boy's material needs in those days. A pack of smokes was still just 20 cents or less. Whenever we could pile into Ron Benjamin's jalopy Chev, we could get as far as a gallon of gas would take us for about the price of the cigarettes. Looking back on the era, it's as though everything -- smokes, gas, bread, meat -- cost about 20 cents, which sometimes was more than we had between us in the pockets of our cotton pants.

That jalopy Chev: It would soon become the prime mover of the adventure, though Duane and I had no way of predicting it as we lounged on the porch steps near the scraps of tree shade on the brown grass of a hot July afternoon, trying to summon the energy for finding something to do.

"Jerry," Duane said, "it's got to be just about time for Mom to be getting home."

"Oh, it's hard to say," I answered. "Sometimes the buses run late, you know. Maybe she stopped at the grocery store. Then she's got a few blocks to walk home."

"I sure wish Mom didn't have to work so hard all the time," Duane said, and I could tell how heartfelt the remark was.

I didn't need to remind my brother that with Mom and Dad separated and our three older brothers in the service, Mom was the only one working.

"You know, Jerry," Duane suddenly said with enthusiasm, "if we could find some kind of work besides hunting golf balls, we could help her out some."

I nodded and thought. What kind of work? That was the problem. Back in the rural community where we were born a kid could work on the farm. In the suburbs, though, there just wasn't much to do.

"It sure would be nice to see him again, wouldn't it?" Duane said.

"Yeah," I agreed, "it sure would. But DeLamere is a long way away. I think the more important thing right now is to find some kind of work to do. Mom might be able to cover the bills, but she sure can't afford to be doling out spending money for us. The least we can do is try to make our own spending money somehow."

Just then Ron Benjamin's jalopy came around the corner. I had to remind Duane not to call it a "jalopy" in front of Benjamin.

"Remember, Duane," I said, "he's touchy about it because he's kinda proud of that Chev. Besides, for now it's just about our only means of transportation, too."

"Wait," Duane reminded me. "At least you've got a bicycle. I don't even have that much."

"Yeah," I granted, "but my bike's just like Ron's car: no front fenders. And every time I ride it in the rain it throws all that water up in my face."

Ron parked the car and got out. The car was a kind of gift Ron's dad had made after Ron turned 16. Cliff Benjamin, a sheet-metal worker, could be strict in a lot of ways. But as long as Ron toed the line he was allowed quite a lot of freedom. And his mobility was the envy of us other guys, who only got to drive cars if we were bold enough to sneak them out after our parents went to bed.

"What's new, guys?" Ron asked, knowing what the answer would be.

"Same old crud, different day," Duane sighed.

I could've said the same. But I didn't. From somewhere a fresh idea suddenly emerged. Maybe it was a combination of seeing the jalopy and thinking about our family, as Duane and I had been doing that afternoon.

"You know, guys," I said, "I just got an idea. We were talking a few minutes ago about trying to find some work. Duane do you remember a couple of years ago before our brothers went into the service, when they went to college for a while in Ellensburg? They told me later that they helped support themselves by working on some of the farms, working in the fields picking potatoes and such. Why couldn't the three of us do something like that?"

It took no time to win an ally in Ron Benjamin.

"Hey, that's a great idea," he said. "We can take some sleeping bags and just sleep out until we make some money to pay for staying some place."

"Jerry," Duane marveled, "I think you've hit it right on the nose. It wouldn't make any difference how much we made. As long as we were supporting ourselves it'd be a great help to Mom."

"Well," I cautioned, "we may not be able to find any work there, so we can't count our chickens yet. But, heck, it would only take a couple of bucks worth of gas to get there and a couple more to get back. I think it's well worth the gamble."

"If we got any serious money," Benjamin mused, "then maybe I could afford bike fenders."

"Gee, what would you want with bike fenders when you've got this jalop-- I mean, this car?" Duane wondered.

"What I mean is motorcycle fenders. I saw some adapted

to a car's front fenders and they looked real neat.''

Benjamin thought about it some more, then said: ''Say, do you guys think you'd mind if Ron Tackett came along? He's Gay's brother -- only 14, but a pretty good guy.''

''Nah,'' I said. ''The more the merrier.''

''By the way,'' Duane said, tentatively, ''what's Gay going to say about you heading out for far-off places?''

Benjamin and Gay had been going together pretty steadily.

''Ah,'' he shrugged, ''I think she'll understand.. ''Look at it this way: If I can come back with a few bucks in my pocket, then at least I'll be able to afford to take her out someplace once in a while--''

He paused and looked over his shoulder.

''Speak of the devil,'' Benjamin said. ''Look who's just walking 'round the corner down there.''

It was Tackett and he looked a little steamed. ''Benjamin,'' he yelled as he approached, ''you passed me way back there and you never even stopped to pick me up. And I yelled at you, too.''

''I never heard you or saw you,'' Benjamin said. ''I guess you're gonna have to learn to yell louder and grow a few inches so I can see you.''

''Hey, forget it, guys,'' I said. ''We've got more important things to discuss right now. Tackett, we've been talking about money, and how we never seem to have any.''

Tackett sighed. ''Try being my age sometime. At least you guys are old enough to get work--''

''Tackett'' I said, ''We tried being your age one time but it turned out to be such an immature age that we just skipped it and went on to the next age.''

Duane and Benjamin only did a fair job of controlling their mirth at the remark.

''Duane,'' Tackett said, ''your brother thinks he's real

funny doesn't he?''

''The trouble is, Tackett,'' Duane said, ''there just aren't any jobs for kids our age. You wait all year for school to get out. Then comes mid-July and there's nothing to do and you're dead broke.''

''Anyway,'' I said, ''the three of us are figuring on going over to Ellensburg to look for some work. Care to go along with us?''

Tackett's eyes widened.

''You guys are serious?''

''If we weren't,'' I smiled, ''we wouldn't have said it. We'll go on over and work in the fields -- maybe pick potatos or whatever they have.''

''Hey,'' he said, ''I'd love to go with you guys.''

''Well,'' I said, ''it's okay with us, but is it going to square with your mom?''

''I can't promise it will,'' Tackett said. ''On the other hand, she's usually pretty agreeable if I'm with you guys. Besides, we really won't be going that far.''

''Nah,'' Duane volunteered. ''It's not like we're going across the country or anything.''

''Maybe a hundred-fifty miles?'' Tackett estimated.

''Great, then,'' I said. I wanted to close the deal as quickly as possible, because I didn't want anybody having second thoughts. This was going to be the adventure of the summer, I could tell, and I quickly said: ''If everyone can get permission, let's figure on leaving first thing in the morning.''

I added: ''I know Duane and I won't have any trouble with permission.'' But I couldn't say so with certainty. We'd still need to sell the deal to Mom when she got home.

We walked out toward the car. I kicked Benjamin's front tire once and wondered if it would last a hundred or so miles. I was the oldest of the bunch, but not by much. Duane, though he was nearly two years younger, already was showing that he'd someday be the better athlete between us. Ron Benjamin might've been a little more mature than me, but only because he had the car. I guess the guys still considered me a leader of sorts, looking up to me kind of the way I had with my older brothers, who'd moved away from home by then. Duane and the two Rons tended to listen to me when I had an idea, and now I spoke pointedly.

"Benjamin," I said, "why not take Tackett home and see if he can go. Then go home and clear it with your folks. If it's all systems go, then call and let us know. Pack up all the gear you guys need and bring it over here. We'll spend the night here and leave first thing in the morning. Got it?"

"Okay, great," Tackett laughed. "Let's get going, Ben."

As they drove off I said: "You know, Duane, I can see why you and I would do this, but if I had a girl like Gay Tackett, I'm not sure I'd be taking off for any place."

Ron Benjamin was always good with girls, where Duane and I were still pretty shy around them, not that we didn't notice them and appreciate what we saw.

"I know what you mean," Duane said. "She sure is a cute little thing."

"It's not called 'little,'" I corrected him. "It's called 'petite.' But you're right. She is cute: that dark brown hair and those dark eyes. Are they dark brown or are they black?"

"Gosh, how would I know," my brother shrugged. "She's never let me get close enough to her to see for sure."

We went in the house to continue making our plans, and in about 45 minutes -- just as Mom appeared up the block -- the phone rang. I can't say I didn't half dread that phone call, because there was the chance the answer from the Rons' parents would be "no." By then Duane and I were convinced we were going to Ellensburg, and nothing was going to stop us -- we hoped.

If so it would be our longest journey in years. It had been about a decade since Dad and Mom packed up all six of us Jacobson kids and moved out to Seattle. That had been the longest trip I could remember, and I doubt Duane could recall any of it at all. Dad had never really taken to life on the West Coast, and when he left the family and returned to North Dakota our mother figured it would be just as well for Duane and me and our little sister Clione to hang back in Seattle. We could get by okay on what Mom made working at a hospital out in Ridgecrest north of Seattle. We had each other and we had the house, which was situated in the kind of timeless neighborhood any kid would remember fondly. Now, nearly half a century removed from the summer of our great adventure, the house and neighborhood, with those '30s-style homes built stout on sturdy foundations, look much the way they did that hot afternoon, when Mom could be seen half a block away.

''Duane,'' I said, ''why not go up the street and help Mom with her groceries, and I'll get the phone. It's got to be Benjamin.''

A case can be made that a major difference between boys and men is that the older they get the longer it takes for them to talk each other into an adventure. By the time you're married and middle-aged, responsibilities always seem to conspire to keep you from making plans to do anything -- taking a fishing trip with the guys, going to a ball game, playing golf. By the time you're 50 you can hardly get together for a quick beer anymore.

But during the summer of '48 we were unencumbered by any responsibilities. Filling our time was itself the major goal for us. Moreover, we were more suggestible than we'd likely ever be. The notion of looking beyond the neighborhood to the great wide outside world would be irresistible, and that's why my idea had met with little resistance.

Sure enough, it was Benjamin on the phone.

"Jerry," he said, excited as I've ever heard him, "the whole thing's a go. Tackett's mom said 'okay,' and so did mine. You know my dad. All he said was: 'Take it easy with that car and don't get into any trouble.' We'll be over at your place after supper.''

Part of the advantage of living where we did was that Mom easily could catch a bus out 15th Avenue north of town, where she worked. Mom would put in long, hard hours at the hospital before catching another bus back down the line to the neighborhood. In those days everybody seemed to use the public transportation, and people were never worried about coming or going at any hour. Violence just wasn't much of an issue back in 1948. That was one reason why our mother wasn't overly concerned about our safety after Duane started pumping her for permission the moment he caught up with her.

"You boys," she sighed, arriving in the kitchen. "I'd worry whether you'd get over there okay in that jalopy. Ron drives it around the neighborhood, but Ellensburg's a long way.''

"Ron's a fine driver, Mom," I countered. "We'd see to it he drove safely, I promise.''

Mom was giving in. She said: "Maybe the car would get you on over there okay. But once you got there, wouldn't you need a place to stay?''

"It'll be hot as Hades over there, Mom," I argued. "We'll sleep outside at night.''

"And eat," she said. "What would you do for food?''

"Aw, Mom," I said. "We'll get by fine. We'll use some

of the money we make to buy food. It'll be cheap at the grocery stores. We won't need to go to restaurants or anything.''

"C'mon, Mom," Duane weighed in. "It's not like we'd be goin' more than a hundred miles or so.''

But I realized that it had to be tough on Mom, what with three kids still home and her being sole support. The last thing in the world I wanted that night was to make her life harder.

Suddenly she turned from being reflective and spoke to me specifically. "Gerald," she said sharply, reminding me how I sometimes hated that name (my middle name was Dean and I could easily be kidded when friends strung the two names together), "if you do this you'll have to promise me you'll look after your brother.''

"C'mon, Mom," I protested, as Duane could barely keep from smiling with the realization that the last two of us had gotten the okay. "Of course I'm going to look after Duane. I always have, haven't I?''

Chapter 2

$\mathcal{T}$hat night we could barely contain ourselves waiting for the Rons to arrive. I knew the other three boys were as eager as they'd ever been about getting away, but I doubted any of them was keener on the adventure than I was. Once we'd all gotten cleared by our parents, I'd have just as soon jumped into the car and drove all night.

As it was, I barely could get to sleep in anticipation of the great adventure: this first chance at going on a real trip in a real car without any grownup supervision. Granted: Guys my age had lied their way into the service and fought in the war a few years earlier. In time I'd grow up and go off with the Army to another continent. My life's travels would lead me from Asia to Spain and Africa, and up to the Great Land of Alaska, where we lived in the decade after statehood. But right now the adventure at hand had me wide-eyed and all smiles as we dreamed about breaking away from the world we'd known.

"All my dad was concerned about," Benjamin reminded us, "was to be sure and drive carefully," and we all knew that the remark hadn't gone unheeded. Mr. Benjamin was a man of few words, and what he said made plenty of impact on Ron and the rest of us.

Still, Tackett couldn't quite resist noting that "at least Mr. B. doesn't have to worry about you denting your front fenders, because you haven't got any."

"I think," Benjamin said, "my Dad's mainly worried about speeding and getting tickets for running stop lights -- things like that. You guys know how dads are."

There was silence for just a few seconds. I wasn't sure whether Benjamin regretted the remark. It's not like Duane and I were all that sensitive about not having Dad at home. It wasn't something we dwelled on, though I think it would've been more important for Duane than for me if Dad had somehow decided to stay on in Seattle, and if he'd wanted to spend the time with us. But the truth was that in 1948, contrary to what people now believe, there were a lot of households with just one parent. A lot of fathers, of course, had died during the war. And even though divorces weren't as common as they are now, they also weren't entirely unheard of. Families also tended to split up. It wasn't at all uncommon for cousins to share a household or for kids to grow up with a "mother" who actually turned out to be an aunt or a second cousin -- or an older sister, for that matter. If it was convenient to make a living arrangement, then that's what you did.

Anyway, Dad wasn't weighing on my mind then. Actually I was recalling what Mom had said when the four of us were about ready to shove off the next morning. She reminded me once again about how I needed to be sure and look after my brother. Then she turned and trundled off toward the bus stop.

"At least let us give you a lift up to work," Benjamin had offered. "We're headed that way."

Mom had waved off the offer, gathering her handbag for the walk to the bus stop.

"I wouldn't ride 10 blocks in that jalopy," she had said to us, "but thanks anyway. And I certainly wouldn't want to ride along as far as you boys are headed."

Where we were headed is kind of hard to imagine when I think back nearly half a century removed. Nowadays we take for granted the Interstate Highway system, but in 1948 the only real auto routes were two-lane roads -- many of them still unpaved. Interstate 5 hadn't yet been built. The main north-south arterial was Highway 99, which stretched in either direction out of Seattle. The first floating bridge linking Seattle with Mercer Island had been completed during the early '40s, and Highway 10, which preceded Interstate 90, went east out of Seattle to Ellensburg. But driving through Seattle, with its traffic problems, didn't appeal to us as much as the scenic Stevens Pass.

So in order to get south and east of Seattle, we'd have to go west and north. And it was with high spirits and a growing sense of adventure that the boys and I made our way across 145th Street west toward 99 on that warm, glorious morning of our first real freedom.

Highway 99, because it was the main travel route, was a seemingly endless string of motels and tourist courts. Many of these old structures have survived to this day. Just behind them along 99 the first post-war suburbs were emerging. Generations of Americans who had lived in city apartments or urban neighborhoods were discovering the advantages of home ownership, and developers were stamping out tract housing in every direction. Within a few years it would seem as though everybody had moved to the suburbs, and every family on every block would seem to have a new baby arriving every year. What had not yet arrived on a large scale in 1948 was television. This was good for several reasons, one of them being that people tended to go out and get together more. Saturday nights really meant something in those days, as people of all ages flocked to dance halls and restaurants and amusement parks and ball fields for their entertainment -- their rewards for having worked what was common then: a six-day week.

Here again, my friends and I would've gladly worked if there'd been jobs. But what could a young kid do to make a living? If your folks had a business of some kind you could work there. There was college if you could get in, but the returning servicemen had a lot of that space tied up -- especially when the GI Bill kicked in and paid their way.

But even if our money-making opportunities weren't so wonderful, I don't think any of the four of us would've traded our place in history with anybody's -- not that morning, anyway.

"You guys hungry?" Benjamin shouted across the car.

"Not me," I yelled back, recalling that I'd actually been way too excited to even eat any breakfast that morning.

"Maybe we'll grab some bread and bologna up through Gold Bar or Index or one of those places," Benjamin said.

Just hearing those vaguely familiar place names was exhilarating, as we all rolled down the windows and laughed and smoked -- masters of all we surveyed.

The car seemed to take forever just to chug up toward Everett, which still was a major smoke-stack town in 1948. Along the way up Rucker we slowed down, passing houses where kids about our age hung out, playing marbles in the morning sun or gawking as we drove by.

"That's what I love most about this trip," Tackett suddenly blurted out to all concerned. "I love it because we're really on the move now. Yesterday we were layin' around like the rest of these kids. Just look at us now."

We must've been quite a sight. If we'd known where fate

was taking us, we probably never would've set out with so few supplies. As it was, we took stock of our inventory after pulling over at a service station in Everett, where we each got a glub of water and relieved ourselves.

Both Rons had brought sleeping bags, but Duane and I had settled for just throwing in a couple of blankets for our bedrolls.

"It's warm as toast all night in Ellensburg," I had assured Mom. "Me and Duane will do just fine with blankets. We'll use our shoes for pillows. We'll be just fine."

As for clothes, we always just wore plain cotton pants and shirts -- not like all the fancy stuff kids wear today. A pair of Oxfords would last us until we outgrew them, and sometimes they were good enough to hand down.

Money? We had about five bucks between us. But that was okay, too. In 1948 you could walk into the finest restaurant in Seattle and get the best meal for less than five dollars. A room at the Olympic Hotel wasn't much more than that. Doctors made housecalls and charged what people could afford to pay (sometimes they didn't charge anything). A reliable second-hand car was a hundred bucks, sometimes less.

So four kids without fancy tastes could get quite a ways on a five spot, especially with 10 gallons of gas in the car and plenty of smokes on board. We also had our hygiene things and spare clothes, and Tackett had brought along a pair of fancy cowboy boots to wear, though none of us could quite figure out why. I couldn't imagine they'd be all that comfortable for field work, but if they made Tackett happy it was fine by me.

What else did we have? We had it made, because most of all we possessed the commodities that money can't buy. We had all the time in the world and we had forward

momentum. Every turn in the road was a new adventure.
Every hamlet and homestead along Highway 2 up through the
valley was an infinite visual improvement on that static life
we'd left behind under the willow trees where we'd lan-
guished -- dying on the summer vines of the North Seattle
neighborhood. It was the sweetest freedom any of us had
known.

And now, as we ran up past Snohomish and along the river
toward Monroe, we all seemed to sense something special
and unprecedented was in the offing for us. Even Tackett,
who had dared to voice a little skepticism that morning, finally
seemed to be in a light mood again.

He had mused for a moment about "what would happen
if we got over to Ellensburg and there just wasn't any work
for us?"

Nobody had responded right away, at which point Tackett
quickly added: "I mean, I can't imagine that would happen,
right Jerry? I mean, we'll find work. I'm sure of that."

Then Benjamin had said: "Of course we will. And even
if we didn't, we'd just turn around and drive on home. We'd
still be broke, but that would be the worst of it, right?"

"But that's not going to happen," Duane said confi-
dently. "We'll find plenty of work and we'll make lots of
money. We won't know what to do with it all, will we Jerry?"

I nodded and smiled. "Anyway," I said a while later, as
we headed into Index, "we'll never get to heaven, will we?"

The remark perked up the other boys' interest, as I knew
it would. Even if we hadn't been inclined toward music it's
very probably our high spirits eventually would've lifted us in
song. But Duane and I were darned fine young singers, or so
we thought back then. The Rons also could harmonize pretty
well, but I was usually the lead singer of the four. We knew
our Mills Brothers tunes verbatim, and we also could sing just

about everything else than came on the radio back during those last years before rock-and-roll rhythms started drowning out the harmonies from popular music.

Our favorite piece by far was a song that must've had hundreds of verses. It seemed as though we never got tired of singing ''Oh, You'll Never Get to Heaven,'' and, sure enough, with perfect spontaneity as we crept past Index on our way up toward the storied railroad town of Skykomish, I raised my baritone voice out the window and launched us into an inspired verse and chorus:

> Oh, you'll never get to heaven
>> (Oh, you'll never get to heaven)
> In a Ford V-8,
>> (In a Ford V-8),
> 'Cause as sure as you're born
>> ('Cause as sure as you're born)
> You're gonna be late.
>> (You're gonna be late).
> Oh, yes you'll never get to heaven
> In a Ford V-8,
> 'Cause sure as you're born
> You're gonna be late.
> I ain't gonna grieve my lord no more
> I ain't gonna grieve my lord no more
> I ain't gonna grieve my lord no more
> I ain't gonna grie-e-e-ve my lord no more.

It was such a rollicking good song that we'd sing it for what seemed like hours on end. Our harmonies were such that we almost made the car windows resonate, as the old Chev climbed up into the Cascades, carrying us off to our destination in Ellensburg. There'd just be Skykomish now, then over Stevens Pass and down into Leavenworth. Then a hard right near Peshastin, south over Blewett Pass and finally the descent into Ellensburg. We were so intoxicated in song that we didn't even notice how little time the great adventure was taking, how briefly we'd been on the road now and how our impending arrival in Ellensburg would mean we'd have to be getting down to business. We would need to be responsible when we got there. We'd have to drive around and poke about and ask questions. The goal was to get some money out of this trip, after all. And fun was fun and all, but Ron Benjamin's dad had reminded us that we needed to think about "taking care of the business at hand."

For the moment, though, we could well afford the giddiness. We were four friends who'd known each other fairly well back in the neighborhood. Now our mission was beginning to bind us into a more important unit. We were all that each of us had for the next few days, and we needed to depend on one another. As the oldest, I felt the keenest sense of needing to be responsible. If anything bad happened, I'd be the one asked first to own up.

Then again, I couldn't fathom anything going wrong. And I wouldn't have wanted to. What was the point in worrying if you didn't have to?

And we certainly didn't have a care in the world -- not, anyway, until Benjamin suddenly cut off the chorus of "Heaven" and did an anxious double-take into his rear-view mirror. What he saw was the last thing any of us anticipated, though it was about to alter our plans -- and maybe even change our lives.

Chapter 3

$\mathcal{J}$ yanked my neck around to see what had startled Benjamin. Out through the narrow rear window of the old Chevy I could see that a car was following pretty closely, and I said so.

"Not just 'A' car," Benjamin said, anxiously. "A squad car. It's the cops."

"But," I protested, "what did we do wrong, Ron?"

"I have no idea," he said, and I could see he was worried.

What had we done? Had we tossed out any lit cigarettes lately? I didn't think so. The ashtray on the dashboard was stubbed full of spent Luckies. "Were we speeding?" I asked Ron.

"This old clunker?" Benjamin said in amazement. "Not likely, not with four of us headed uphill."

But within seconds the siren was wailing and the red light on the patrol car was turning, turning, turning: waving us down.

The officer seemed friendly enough at the outset. He was a portly fellow, tightly put into his police jodphurs and a creased shirt that held up the badge.

"You the owner of this vehicle?" he asked Benjamin.

"I am," Ron said. "My dad and me. Anything wrong,

officer?''

''Two things,'' the cop quickly said. ''You got your driver's license?''

''Yessir,'' Ron said smartly, fumbling for his wallet.

The officer sized him up slyly and said: ''Can you guess which two things I'm talking about?''

Benjamin scratched his head and didn't answer, but I think the rest of us could tell what was coming.

''In this state,'' the officer said as though he were a driving instructor, ''a legal car must have front fenders. This car doesn't have any.''

Benjamin then smiled widely and surveyed the rest of us in the car. No problem, he seemed to assure us, winking.

''See, officer,'' he grinned, ''that's exactly why we're on this trip. You hit it right on the head. My buddies and me, we're headed for Ellensburg -- be there in just another hour or so. When we make some money in the fruit harvest we'll buy fenders first thing. That's the whole point.''

The officer said nothing, then sidled back to the cab of his squad car. We couldn't see him writing anything, so we allowed ourselves to assume he'd seen things our way.

Then Duane said: ''Hey, he's on the radio. Who's he talkin' to?''

In a minute we found out when he returned to Benjamin's window and said: ''You boys'll need to wait here a while 'til the tow truck gets up here.''

Benjamin was in disbelief. ''Tow truck?'' he repeated. ''But we're not out of gas. The car drives just fine.''

''Well,'' the cop said. ''It doesn't drive just fine. Got no front fenders that's what. Drive this car and it could kick up gravel -- maybe break somebody's windshield and cause a major traffic accident. That's why the law says 'mandatory,' son.''

Perhaps it's comforting to recall in retrospect that boyhood and adolescence are when mere minutes can divide flying at the heights and crashing to the depths. Never, though, had any of us known anything this devastating. One minute we're gliding up the highway, singing at the tops of our lungs under the glimmer of Mt. Index on our way to the crest of the Cascades. The next minute not only are we stopped and lectured. Now the police department is impounding our car.

"They can't get away with this," Benjamin assured one and all after the tow truck had picked up the rear of the Chevy and hustled into town behind the flashing light of the patrol car. We must've looked like a parade to the locals, who were going about their business.

"Welcome to Skykomish," Tackett cracked sarcastically, as we got out at the gas station where the car had been taken.

The cop spoke privately for a minute with the tow driver, and we could see they were pretty amused by the sight of us four boys. Then the officer returned to our group and laid down the law.

"You fellas remember now," he lectured, "that you have no business driving the state roads with a vehicle in this condition. Now I'm locking up this vehicle until you and your dad can make arrangements to get it safely back to Seattle."

I had an idea.

"Officer," I said, "supposing we could get some fenders put on here in Skykomish. Then could we get the car back?"

The cop thought it over.

"I s'pose," he finally reckoned. "Only the nearest wrecking yard that I know of is back down in Monroe. You boys want to walk down to Monroe and back up the mountain? Fine by me, fellas, but I should tell you it's about 40 miles each way -- the uphill way being the hardest, expecially when you're carryin' a couple of Chev fenders.''

Instead we walked through Skykomish, stunned by the turn of events. Benjamin was more mad than anything.

''I drive that darned Chevy all over North Seattle and never once get stopped,'' he recalled. ''Then this. Well, what I'm half tempted to do is go back after dark and get my car back.''

Duane said: ''Hot-wire your own car?''

''Naw,'' Benjamin said. ''I got a spare key wired under the engine. Wouldn't take but a second.''

But we all knew this wasn't feasible. For one thing, the cop had warned us about coming around where the car was impounded. More important: We weren't the sort of kids to do anything that would deliberately break the law. I'm not saying we accepted our predicament. Far from it. Each one of us in turn bemoaned what had happened: how we were so close to getting through Skykomish and on up over Blewett; how we'd easily have made Ellensburg by early afternoon but . . .

''Why did this have to happen,'' I yelled, scuffing the dirt.

We walked aimlessly, silently. It was hard to believe we'd been singing an hour earlier -- hard to imagine we'd ever sing again. As the nominal leader, I realized we were going to have to come up with some decisions pretty soon. I ran them through my head.

Probably the practical thing would be to contact Mr. Benjamin after he got home from work in Seattle. We could wire him from the Skykomish post office, but boy he'd be mad if he had to miss a work day and come up and take care of this mess. And I guess we wouldn't have blamed him.

I remembered at least one close call with Cliff Benjamin. Back when Ron and I were first getting interested in cars, sometimes we'd arrange to sleep out on a nice night. Then, after Mr. and Mrs. Benjamin turned in, Ron and I would go to work. Mr. Benjamin had this '37 Ford that was really light and easy to push. To us it was a regular chariot, and every chance we got we'd sneak into the front seat and figure out all the sticks and knobs. It's difficult to believe looking back on it from a time when people buy theft alarms for their cars. But that Ford was one of those cars that could be started with a flip switch instead of an ignition key. Anybody could've driven off with it, but the times weren't like that, not in 1948, when people left their doors unlocked -- and left everybody else alone.

Those warm nights, under the stars, the car was always parked on the other side of the house from the bedroom windows. We'd release the hand brake and quietly roll the sedan out into the street. That time of night it usually was so still you could hear twigs crack under the fat tires. Then we'd shove the car half a block until we were far enough away to start the engine. And for a few precious minutes we'd be on the road, driving on our own. The neighborhood would be all ours.

That's the way it was, anyway, except for one night in particular. Shoving the car out of the driveway, we looked back to see Mr. B standing at the front door.

"Just what are you boys doing out there?" he wanted to know, never raising his firm voice -- then or ever, to my recollection.

"Uh, well," Ron stammered, "we're, uh, just pushing the car back and forth."

Mr. Benjamin considered Ron's explanation -- Ron, who must've sensed how lame his remark had been. I guess we don't quite fathom it until we grow up with kids of our own, but dads were young sons once themselves, and Ron's dad said:

"I sure can't see how you boys can get any kick out of pushing a car back and forth. But since you've already pushed it back, I suggest you now push it forth. And leave it forth."

I don't know about Ron, but for a second I actually believed his explanation had satisfied his dad. That belief quickly ended, when Mr. B added:

"In the future, any time that I look out here, whether it be later tonight or any other night, I expect the car to be in the 'forth' position. Do you understand?"

Then he turned back into the house, knowing that his pronouncement had made the intended point. Within two minutes the Ford was pushed "forth," where it remained every night thereafter.

Did I envy Ron Benjamin having to tell his dad about the impounding? No more than I relished our predicament, which we assessed after crossing the Skykomish Bridge above the trickling summer run glittering in the sunlight. We flopped down on a grassy spot near the railroad tracks.

Skykomish had made itself necessary after the great James J. Hill decided in 1889 to extend his Great Northern Railroad to the West Coast -- and do so without the benefit of government money. That led Hill to make the acquaintance of the fabulous location engineer John F. Stevens, who later in life would help build the Panama Canal and reorganize the China-Trans-Siberian Railroad. It became Stevens' challenge to find a way over the Montana Rockies (thus the discovery of Marias Pass), then find a similar route through the Cascades. Stevens Pass, as it came to be known, was found 17 miles east of Skykomish, meaning the new town would grow in stature as a center for logging and mining.

It also meant something else for Skykomish. Stevens' trans-Cascades project wouldn't be possible without tunneling the mountain. The tunnel proved to be eight miles long, but during the early years after the project was completed there was no existing technology to ventilate such an underground span. With no ventilation, steam and diesel engines would choke and asphyxiate anybody aboard the trains.

The solution was to outfit trains with electric engines for the trips through the tunnel. Consequently, Skykomish became the west-side location for outfitting eastbound Great Northern trains with the clean electric engines, which would travel up through the tunnel and down into Wenatchee. There the eastbound trains would be refit with diesel or steam engines. Westbound traffic would take on electric engines in Wenatchee and trade back in Skykomish.

All this activity prompted considerable commerce in Skykomish, which we admired as we lay around thinking about our options.

"I guess," I finally concluded, "we'll just have to thumb to Ellensburg. It won't be easy, but I don't know what else to do. It's pretty plain we can't walk the rest of the way."

"Yeah," Duane said, "but that would mean splitting up, wouldn't it?"

"We couldn't all expect to get a ride in the same car," Tackett reasoned.

But Benjamin was hesitant. "Hey," he reminded us, "the whole point of going to Ellensburg was to go over together. In one car. Now look at us. I guess I've put it off long enough. I'd better head over to the post office and see about letting my dad know we got as far as Skykomish before disaster happened."

I suddenly became more aware of the railroad yard before us: the tangles of tight wires strung up everywhere above the railroad tracks. I squinted for a minute and the whole scene -- the acres and acres of railroad yard -- looked like a picture from a book. My idea of electric trains had been those toy Lionel models, the ones that ran on the power the transformer sent through the tracks. I'd heard about the tremendous engineering accomplishments that made Skykomish possible, but it had never really sunk in. The long tunnel through the Cascades -- longest of its kind, we'd heard -- didn't seem real to us. What seemed real was Alan Ladd defending Burma Road to the death during a movie matinee back in the early '40s. Alan Ladd. ''Burma Road.'' High adventure!

I must've been staring pretty hard, because suddenly Duane interrupted my daydream.

''Jerry,'' he said. ''You look like you're thinking a hole right through the sky, doesn't he Tackett?''

Tackett grinned at me. ''Somebody give Jerry a cigarette,'' he said. ''I think he's got an idea.''

And I did. Was it a good one? How did I know? Had it been a smart plan to jump into a jalopy with no front fenders and head off for a place we'd never been to get jobs we didn't know would be waiting for us? Was there such a thing as a good idea among boys who were 14, 15, 16 and 17, and who weren't yet men? Boys whose idea of ''real'' adventure was what Alan Ladd had done on screen? We were kids, after all, who plainly couldn't see the best opportunity for the greatest thrills of our lives, even though it sat dead square in front of us.

''I'll take that smoke,'' I said to Tackett, and he tossed us all Luckies and we all sat and puffed.

''I've been thinking this over,'' I finally said. ''What are we out right now?''

''Just a car, that's all,'' Tackett cracked.

''Naw,'' I said. ''We're not out a car.''

''C'mon, Jerry,'' Duane said, ''we've already been over

that. We go back tonight and take that car out of hock and the cops will be on us like Pretty Boy Floyd.''

"Right," I said. "So we forget about the car for now."

"Fine," Benjamin said. "I nominate you to tell my dad to forget about the car."

"Because," I continued, paying no attention to any of them, "it isn't the car that we're out right now. If we can carry our belongings, then all we really need is transportation."

"Great," Tackett laughed. "I'll call us a cab."

"Don't need one," I smiled, gesturing with exaggerated majesty down toward the railroad yards. "Not when we can hop a freight."

Chapter 4

The pause worried me. I don't know whether I was worried they'd say "no" or afraid they'd say "yes." But I realized for the first time in my life that there's never anything quite so wonderfully terrifying as the moment when a boy -- or man -- takes an outrageous idea and proposes it out loud. In five simple words I had proposed a notion that all of us would've laughed at just an hour earlier. If I'd made the remark a week earlier the guys would've thought I'd taken leave of my senses.

But here we were: stuck in Skykomish with no forward momentum and no happy prospects for turning back toward Seattle. And I had said it:

"We can hop a freight."

And scarier yet: What I'd said was the flat truth.

Benjamin was the first to respond as we lay there in the grass, eyeing one another, glancing furtively toward the railroad tracks.

"Jerry," he said, "you're really crazy, you know that?"

"No, I'm not," I protested. "What I am is stuck in a small town without transportation."

Duane said: "You're right about one thing, Jerry. What we have here isn't so much a car problem as a transportation problem.''

Tackett said: ''If that's the case, maybe we oughta wait for the next passenger train to come through and we can buy first-class tickets over to Ellensburg. Probably only set us back $20 apiece.''

''No, wise guy,'' I said. ''We'll ride for free. And it'll be a lot more fun than any darned passenger car.''

Benjamin scarcely was convinced. ''You ever hop a train, Jerry?'' he asked, knowing the answer already.

I was about to concede the point when Duane spoke up. ''Aw, Ron,'' he said, ''that's the least of our worries. We've seen it done lots of times in the movies. Millions of times.''

But Tackett was skeptical. ''Understand, now,'' he said. ''It's not that I'm scared or anything, because I'm not. I'd probably do it, but there's other things to worry about.''

''Like what?'' I pressed him. ''You wait 'til nobody's looking and you hop onto a nice boxcar. It's like having your own private car, only there aren't any porters or conductors or anybody around to bother you. C'mon, it'll be a cinch.''

''Yeah,'' Tackett started, ''but what about the railroad dicks?''

Duane chuckled for a second. ''The whats?''

''Railroad detectives,'' Benjamin said, seriously. ''They ride the trains and kick off the hoboes. I think they wear guns.''

''Okay,'' I said, ''first of all let's say there really are detectives. What's the worst they can do? Kick us off the train, right? But we're only going as far as Ellensburg, so what are the odds?''

''Yeah,'' Duane said, ''that's right. What can happen between here and Ellensburg?''

''Well,'' Tackett sighed, ''when you look at what's happened between Seattle and Skykomish, I guess about anything, Duane.''

"But look at it this way," I said. "We go back to Seattle with our tails between our legs and we have to face Mr. Benjamin. And we still won't have made any dough."

"Besides," Benjamin noted, "when I think of who I'd rather face right now between a railroad dick and my dad, I guess it isn't even close. You guys are lucky, Jerry and Duane, because your dad's back in North Dakota where he can't keep an eye on you."

Were we really so lucky? I can't speak for Duane, but I know it would've been better to have had even a strict dad at home rather than none at all. But Duane and I compensated pretty well. Being brothers so close in age made us close in how we behaved. Neither of us ever would've considered hopping a freight train if we'd thought there was something terribly wrong about it. But here we were: presented with the perfect opportunity for adventure, and just when we needed to pick up the pace and freshen a trip that suddenly had gone sour. A day earlier the idea of hopping a freight would've seemed ridiculous. We would've packed off the idea to that realm beyond the reach of the armchair adventurer, that fantastic place filled with the exploits you only read about. It would've been just one more thing you never considered, one more thing that only "the other people" do.

And, of course, there was another problem. I'd promised Mom that I would look after Duane. Mom hadn't been all that sold on the auto trip, and I can but imagine what she'd have said about my latest idea. I could just hear myself: "So, Mom, I think I'll take Duane and we'll, ya know, jump aboard a moving railroad car and head up over the mountains." That's how crazy the idea sounded. Yet that's precisely what we boys nearly had agreed to do.

"There's one other minor detail," Tackett said. "What

happens if one of us falls off the train?''

But Duane was ready for him. ''Nothing happens,'' my brother smiled, ''because we just don't fall off, that's all.''

''Yeah,'' I said, not quite sure of myself, ''because we wouldn't even think of doing this if we thought we were going to fall off . . . would we?''

I don't know how convincing I sounded. Duane was gung-ho, but the Rons still seemed skeptical. Nobody spoke for a minute. Then Benjamin said: ''Well, if we're really gonna do it, then I guess I'd best get over to the post office and drop my dad a card.''

''Maybe I'll go with you,'' Tackett said.

''Let's all go,'' I proposed. ''We can stop at the store and pick up some smokes and eats.''

''The more I think of it,'' Benjamin said, as we got up with a bounce in our steps, ''I feel better about this already. Just knowing I'm not going to have to deal with Dad for a few more days puts a new shine on this day.''

''Yeah,'' Duane added, ''and it also means we don't have to split up.''

But we did anyway, temporarily. The Rons went and sent the post card and Duane and I spent some of the precious remaining cash on a couple of packs of cigarettes and some candy bars. As we sat on a bench out in front of the store waiting for the Rons to get back I became aware of the businesslike activity of the Skykomish townfolk. They were all coming and going, heedless of our predicament and our plans. At one point a new Chrysler station wagon with the wood side paneling glided by and inside I could see a coupla-three kids about our ages. Their parents were in the front seat and the kids were situated around the back. They stared out the windows at us and I stared back.

Seeing these kids in tow with their folks made me appre-

ciate just how on our own the four of us really were. I
suddenly realized that if we got on that train we would be
taking a much larger step than just climbing onto the rung of
a railroad ladder. We'd also be stepping out of the level of our
experience. This wouldn't be like it had been squeezing onto
a golf course, though I remembered the first time we'd done
that and how the adrenalin had run from realizing we'd gotten
away with it. First you had to come into Jackson Park from
the road through a bunch of brush and trees, where grown
men hung around looking for lost golf balls. You had to be
sure and bring a few clubs along: odd irons, a one wood and
a putter. Then you had to wait for some slack between
groups. Sometimes you could wait for an hour or more before
an opportunity presented itself. When it happened you just
came out and started playing toward the hole as if you
belonged there. If the grown-up players caught on, the worst
that would happen is that they'd make you leave. But sometimes we could sneak in several holes without getting detected, and a lot of the time the golf experiences we valued
most were the sweet shots we made when we were playing
for free.

Sneaking some golf was something lots of the kids did.
None that I know of ever had sneaked a ride on a freight train,
as we were about to do -- or attempt to do. For the fact of
the matter was, as the Rons returned and we headed back
toward the freight yards, I had to admit to myself that I
genuinely was not sure about how this adventure was going
to work. I imagined hopping a freight had to be not much
different from how Jackie Cooper or Mickey Rooney did it in
the movies. Didn't you just wait for the train to start moving,
grab hold of something and pull yourself up? I had to concede
to myself that I really had no clue, and Tackett, always the
skeptic, seemed to read my mind.

"Now that we're really gonna do this," he was saying as we walked to the eastern terminus of the yards and waited in the nearby woods, "maybe Jerry will explain HOW we're gonna do it."

I realized that the boys doubtless were taking a cue from my confidence level, so I acted as though I knew what I was doing.

"First," I said, trying to approximate the manner of a freight-hopping instructor, "it's important that we have our grip tied together so we can sling it over our backs. We'll need both hands and feet free for climbing aboard."

How the boys figured I'd come by this hobo wisdom was beyond me, but confidence was a burden of being the eldest of the group, and they responded by taking a professional attitude in their preparations. Tackett was the most keen on seeing to it that his grip was secure, seeing as how he'd brought a brand-new pair of cowboy boots -- which he made a great point of reminding everybody (even though none of us could figure how he planned to do any work in stiff, new boots). Between us we had the two sleeping bags, a few blankets, extra clothes and scant personal items. Upon leaving Seattle we hadn't planned on having to consolidate all this stuff into portable baggage, but within half an hour we had everything pretty well tied down.

"Now what?" Benjamin asked as we all sat down and lit up a smoke.

"Now," I said, "we just wait here for our ride to arrive."

We sat quietly for about five minutes, then started making small talk unrelated to the task at hand. We talked about other kids back in the neighborhood and we talked about songs and cars. I mentioned to the boys the Chrysler Woody I'd seen earlier, and gradually the car talk steered us back to the impending adventure.

Suddenly Duane started to laugh.

"What's funny?" Tackett wanted to know.

"What's funny," Duane said, "is that we're really gonna do this, aren't we?"

We were, I thought, if the right train would ever come through the yard. I realized that momentum was a precious commodity in sustaining an adventure. And, while none of the other three (certainly not Duane) was about to break ranks, I also wanted to see to it everybody got on the train. That way there could be no looking back. That way we'd never be able to regret not going on this adventure.

But the wait gradually grew tedious. Several times one or more of the boys got up and walked to the clearing straining to see if a train was about to arrive.

"Relax," I said. "Be patient. All the trains come through here. There isn't any other way."

Then, when the lull had become unbearable even for me, along through Skykomish it came: a Great Northern freight from the west, with a diesel engine pulling what seemed to be cars stretching halfway back down to Everett.

"Boys," I shouted, as the train chugged to a standstill to get outfitted with its electric engine for the tunnel, "I believe our ride has arrived."

We were cautious as we came in along the tracks, parallel to the train. Teenage boys have that practiced way of trying to appear nonchalant, even when their behavior tells the rest of the world that they clearly have no idea what's going on. We sauntered along the tracks, shouldering our gear and inspecting the various hoppers and stock cars and boxes and tanks and flats. The appearance we were trying to project was that of four kids who just happened to be wandering around near a soon-to-be-departing train -- four kids, mind you, who had no thought of actually hopping a moving freight.

Any adult observer would've had our intentions spotted in an instant: That much I've since learned.

With our inexperience, though, we had no way of knowing that there would be few if any observers. For all the activity in a freight yard, it's actually rare to ever see very many men working.

Soon the engines had been switched, but there was still a disturbing lack of activity.

"Do we get on now?" Duane wondered.

"No," I said, still trying to project assuredness, but without any real-world authority to back it up, "I think we wait until the train starts to move. I think that's the way it's done."

Let's say I hoped and prayed that's how it was done, because suddenly the train was moving. Very gradually, like a baby starting to crawl, it was tending eastward. But we hadn't yet found a suitable car. A boxcar would've been the ideal vehicle because it would be safe and enclosed. But none of the boxcars was open. Worse yet: No flatcars could be seen. The engine disappeared in the distance, but the train was so long that the caboose wasn't yet visible on the approach.

"It's time, fellas," I shouted above the gathering freight-yard din.

"But," Benjamin yelled, "there's no car to climb onto."

"I know," I shouted. "We'll have to grab ladders and ride between boxcars."

Tackett yelled: "But that's dangerous."

"C'mon," I shouted to the others, as the cars started picking up speed. "You've got good tread on your shoes. Grab the ladder rungs and get aboard. It's now or never."

It was now. Four young men cinched their gear tight and, running alongside of the train, grabbed with their hands and flung their bodies between boxcars.

I was the last to board.

''We're all on!'' I shouted, triumphantly. ''Everybody hang on for dear life.''

''Goodbye, cruel world,'' Tackett yelled, wise-cracking to the end.

Chapter 5

*J*t had all just been a dream, a fantasy, a stunt that boys do on a whim or a dare. I don't know whether any of us actually visualized grabbing those cold steel rungs and climbing aboard a freight train. What was it going to be like? Like Tom Joad hitting the rails in "The Grapes of Wrath"? That's what we'd wondered an hour earlier, when the whole notion of actually getting hold of something that was moving, something infinitely bigger than ourselves, had still been just an idea that resided in the safe place of dreams.

But not anymore. Suddenly we were amateurs no more, as the train steadily picked up speed and we clung to our precarious perches.

Riding as we were was a novelty, but it wasn't the most comfortable way to go. Nor was it anything resembling safe. We were positioned sort of like trapeze artists. Ron Benjamin was high up on the boxcar ladder, clinging like a bird clawing a cage. Then came Tackett, situated below Benjamin and just as inclined to keep a tight squeeze on his rung. Duane and I had the trickiest position, standing as we were on a coupling between the boxcars. There was an expanse of about 18 inches where a person could place his shoes. Then you hung onto the nearest boxcar rungs, only looking down to get a grim appreciation of what a slip of the shoe leather could mean.

The coupling, after all, only rode a few feet above the track. When I looked down I could just about memorize every fishplate and joint bar, every sleeper tie and baseplate, every spike head that stuck up out of the ballast bed. I did not want any part of slipping into the abyss, but the train seemed to want otherwise. As it listed and swayed, heading toward the top of the Cascades, the coupling plate shifted, giving the jiggling effect you sometimes feel while riding in the safer parts of the train. As it was, I sort of felt the same jeopardy a dog must sense while getting jostled in a pickup-truck bed over bad road.

''You fellas okay up there?'' I shouted toward the top rung.

Benjamin was laughing now, and I knew he was all right. It relieved me to see Benjamin enjoying himself, because I knew how disappointed he'd been about the car episode. Here it was: his first road trip driving on his own, and suddenly no car.

Ah, but now there was the railroad. So what if three of us were stuck so low between cars that we couldn't see more than a trace of the passing scenery: the whoosh of the woods alongside the railroad beds, the occasional scrapped car showing up orange and ugly through the stunted firs. So what if the gear was gripping us and keeping us from getting comfortable. We were moving again. We were together. And we were all wide smiles, a riot of great boyish fun.

It would've made quite a sight to any onlooker, but there wasn't much chance of encountering anybody. After passing the eastern outskirts of Skykomish you hit dead sylvan wilderness all the way up to Stevens Pass, 3,000 feet above sea level. There would be no percentage now in getting off the train for any reason. I hadn't really thought it through, but it seemed to me the trip over the mountains would be such an ordeal for the railroad workers that they'd never take time to check and see whether anybody had stowed away out of Skykomish.

No, being discovered was the least of our worries, as I shifted my weight once and listened to the unmistakable rhythm only a train can make.

"Ellensburg, here we come!" Tackett shouted.

"Amen!" Duane yelled.

Duane's delight with the adventure was very satisfying for me. But I also had a nagging worry that something dreadful would happen and that it would be my fault. Gosh, if only mother could see us now. Late in the afternoon, Mom would be working away at the hospital, thinking about getting home to Clione. Maybe she sent a stray thought toward Duane and me, consoling herself with the mental picture of us four roughnecks singing at the tops of our lungs as we barreled down into Ellensburg, safe as we could be inside of Benjamin's jalopy Chev. If so, was she ever wrong.

The rungs of the boxcar suddenly felt a little sweaty in my palms, and I realized I was squeezing them excessively. I looked over at Duane and he was doing the same.

"We're strangling the clubs, Duane," I laughed, referring to a mistake beginners often make playing golf. You're never supposed to squeeze the golf club too hard, but Duane picked right up on my meaning when he said:

"This is one club I don't mind strangling."

The train had picked up pretty good speed now -- was chugging along at a pace that would've precluded jumping off safely.

"How long 'til we get to the top?" Tackett shouted.

"I don't know," I yelled up to him, catching myself before adding: "But don't we have to pass the tunnel first?"

The tunnel: Back in Skykomish I hadn't really thought about it and I guess I had no idea of what to expect. We'd gone through tunnels at home in Seattle, but always in cars. The Mount Baker tunnel south of town had been finished in 1941 and had quickly developed into a tourist destination. It was narrow and spooky, and newspaper reports had told of how people with claustrophobia hadn't taken kindly to slow driving through this hole in the ground. But the Mount Baker tunnel was lit. If you thought of it as just being like driving at night with your lights on, then it didn't offer any great cause for emotional alarm, not for Duane and me, anyway.

But then there was the question of the Cascade Tunnel. We had learned about it in school. It was a wonder of engineering, this spelunking expedition through eight miles of a hard-rock mountain range. Folks came from hundreds of miles to see the historical markers and read about the achievement, and those who had traveled through the underground passage were the envy of their friends when they told of the adventure.

But how many had passed through while standing outdoors on ladders? I don't know whether I had enough warning to even wonder, as Benjamin suddenly pulled his head down from above the boxcar and frantically shouted down to us:

"Hey, you guys, the tunnel's just up ahead!"

It would envelope us in a matter of moments. I nearly panicked, but I gathered my wits in time to yell a few orders.

"Benjamin and Tackett," I shouted. "You've got to climb up almost to the top of the ladder and make room for Duane and me."

Tackett started quickly but one of his feet slipped off the rung and he held on with both hands for dear life.

"Careful," I yelled. "We can't make any mistakes now."

Tackett gathered himself and scrambled back up the ladder, tucking himself just below Benjamin.

I shouted to the top: "Benjamin, you've got to watch yourself up there."

My worry was that if one of us slipped then maybe we'd all fall. I sent Duane up from the coupling.

"Okay, everybody," I shouted, "we can't just expect to hang on with our fingers and make it through. Wrap your arms through the ladder and hang onto the backs of the rungs. Fingers will get tired much faster than arms."

I shouldn't have done it, but I strained my head around the side of the boxcar to see if I could get a sense of how quickly we were approaching the tunnel. The rusty metal casing of the boxcar scraped my face, and my eyes teared. Everything was a blur all of a sudden. I took a hand from the rung and reached my shirt across my eyes. Barely, in the distance, I could make out the face of the mountain coming at us. The train was positioned so that the tracks were tending to the left toward the tunnel, and all I could see was the narrow slit of blackness between the train and the opening. In seconds we'd be absorbed by the thing, and I still hadn't gotten myself safely above the coupling.

"Jerry," Duane yelled down to me, "c'mon. Take care of yourself."

But then it was pitch black. I'd known total darkness just one other time. At some cousins' house back in North Dakota, when I was just a little kid, I'd wandered down to the cellar to look around. This was the Great Depression era, and if you left on any light switches needlessly it was practically a high crime. All I remember now is hearing the slam of a door from the kitchen to the cellar. I was immersed in darkness of such intensity that my inner eyes actually seemed to see white hot with fear for a moment. Then I guess I screamed with such fury that the relative who had shut off the light switch was persuaded that there really had been someone in the cellar. So instead of getting into trouble for leaving the light on, I got an apology.

And I got very scared, too. I knew that I never wanted to witness total blackness again, but suddenly, in a chugging instant of locomotive time, there we were: sightless in an eight-mile stone tomb.

With nowhere to go, the intense noise from the train ricocheted in infinite variety back and forth off the tunnel walls. It took a few seconds for me to get my footing fixed above the coupling. Then, one by one, I shouted out a desperate roll call.

"Benjamin?" I yelled. "Call back if you're all right."

Seconds went by. Then he finally responded: "I think so, Jerry, but I'm not liking this."

"Tackett?" I yelled. "Present, teacher." He was wisecracking again, so I knew he must be okay, especially when he added: "Can we pull up the window shades now?"

Duane I didn't have to call. I could feel his leg tucked in above my shoulder. Duane was plenty strong enough to hold on long enough to stay the course. So was I. My greatest worry was that the train might start shimmying again. In total blackness the eye soon starts playing tricks with the other senses. It fools the ear, and that affects the balance. I had no idea how many travel minutes eight miles of tunnel translated to. It was a full train headed uphill, so it could only pull at about 14 miles an hour. But who knew what speed we were going in total darkness? And how long would it take to get through eight miles at a rate of 14 mph? It didn't do to work math problems at the moment. What I did know was that if anybody's balance was challenged, then chances were pretty good one of us would lose a grip. If that happened . . .

$\mathcal{J}$ guess it wasn't even worth thinking about what such an eventuality would mean. There had been those railroad tracks below us, beckoning the odd slip of shoe leather. I'd once read about a train mishap: how a kid on a bike had gotten his tire stuck in a railroad-track tie plate after having gotten his pant leg caught in the tire chain. What were the odds? In those days, if you didn't have a chain guard on your bike, then you rolled up the pant leg high enough so that it wouldn't catch the chain. But this was just a little kid: 8-year-old, I think. And the train didn't stop. And it dragged the poor little guy under and . . .

And it didn't do to imagine what one slip in this awful blackness would mean.

"Everybody okay then?" I tried not to sound overly worried.

"Yep."

"I'm okay."

"Unh-huh."

"So far, so good, then," I yelled back. "But we'd better all be quiet now, so if anything happens to any of us we'll be able to hear. Now listen, though. If anybody starts to feel weak or thinks they're maybe having a problem, say so right away. Don't wait 'til it's too late."

But I knew my instruction might be next to useless. I could feel Duane, but I had no contact with the other two. If

Benjamin or Tackett started to slip, there'd be no chance of
me grabbing for them in the blackness. Even if Duane started
to go, what could I do? The steel rungs, grown cold now, were
difficult enough for me to grasp. How could I hang on with
one hand and support Duane with the other?

"I guess it's too late to get off this ride," Tackett
shouted, and I didn't even want to respond.

A moving train outside of a tunnel would be tricky enough
to evacuate. Inside the tunnel there had to be no more than a
few feet of clearance in either direction. Even if a guy could
get off safely, you'd wander endlessly in the pitch blackness
until the next train came along and put you out of your misery.

No, there was nothing to do but cling and hope. Suddenly
I felt Duane's weight shift.

"Duane!" I screamed. "Don't move! You falling?"

"Sorry," he shouted back. "I was changing my grip."

"This is getting kind of tiresome," Tackett yelled. "I'm
freezing in here."

"Just hold on," I shouted. "Everybody hold on. It can't
be much longer."

But it was. It was the longest eight miles any of us had
ever traveled. Ten minutes went by. In the total blackness I
started seeing phantoms in my imagination. Walking would've
seemed faster, and the burden of the gear tearing at our sides
was becoming just as unbearable as being blind.

Another 10 minutes passed and suddenly Benjamin shouted
down to us. He sounded very scared, yelling: "It's gotta pass
pretty soon."

"Hang on!" I yelled.

Suddenly the clatter of the tracks was muffled and the
light and air hit us like shock waves from a bomb.

"God bless it," Tackett marveled. "It's like coming out
of a movie."

The gray sylvan greenery with filtered sunlight was like Eden as our eyes smarted and stung, slowly adjusting.

"That," Benjamin yelled, "was the scariest movie I've ever seen."

But Duane, always game, laughed and whooped. "C'mon, guys," he shouted. "Let's turn around and go back through!"

Chapter 6

$\mathcal{I}$f it took a few minutes for our eyes to readjust to the wondrous sunlight, our noses knew in an instant that we'd finally emerged from that sulfurous mountain tomb. The Cascade Tunnel didn't get a ventilation system until eight years after we passed through on that thrill ride of a lifetime. Without proper ventilation, travelers could still breathe the tunnel air without suffocating or being poisoned. The electric engines saw to that. But inside the tunnel it didn't smell nearly as sweet as the fragrances wafting from the summer leaves and fir boughs as we trundled down the Tumwater canyon and abruptly came out of the mountains.

Our hands were sore as though we'd done a week's worth of chores. The four of us literally had hung on for dear life during that seemingly interminable trip through the chasm of blackness. Now that we could see things clearly, we still understood that there was no call for recklessness. Perched where we were between boxcars, we still needed to be as careful as always, lest one of us fall and take one or more of the others with him. The enormous train wheels, cutting like saw blades, were fixed just below us between boxcars.

But we were bound for our destination, and that made the pain in our hands and limbs much more bearable. We loosened up and laughed about having survived the tunnel, and I got the indication Duane really would've plunged back in for a rerun if he'd had the chance. It was like going on a rollercoaster for the very first time: fearing it, yet loving it and wanting to do it again.

As we headed down toward orchard territory I suddenly had the nagging awareness that the fun would soon end. We'd get to Ellensburg and probably find work somewhere, toiling away at some man's truck farm or cherry orchard, the dawn-to-dusk drudgery eased only by the knowledge that we'd have plenty of tobacco and sandwich money in our pants by the end of each day. But nothing I could imagine about farm work was even remotely as joyous and romantic as the recent hour had been. When I'd first proposed hopping the rails it had been with the understanding it would be the only expedient way to get from Point A to Point B. Never had it occurred to me that there would be the added benefit all four of us had truly come to appreciate: that it would be some of the greatest sheer fun we'd ever had.

"We're coming into fruit country now," I yelled up to the others.

"I'll reach out and pick us off some apples," Duane joked.

"Make mine red delicious," Tackett deadpanned. "If they don't have any red delicious, then I don't want any at all."

Benjamin continued riding at the top of the boxcar ladder.

"Watch out for train detectives," I yelled up to him.

"If you see me jump off," he shouted back, "that's how you'll know you'd better bail out too."

But there weren't any train detectives. Nor were there any brakemen or engineers. Riding along in anonymity, it was as though we owned the train outright. There was no visible clue that anybody else was aboard. It was like riding on some great horse -- the iron horse -- that was carrying us off like we were in some storybook adventure.

And now there was the perfect scenery for the story. The train coursed along near Highway 2, but its tracks ran far enough from the road so that we sensed we were in the middle of uncharted territory. Then the rich, dense, lush orchards started to emerge as we swept down through Leavenworth and the Peshastin-Dryden area toward Cashmere. Years later I'd learn of the swaying that caused a derailment near Peshastin in 1928, and I'd shudder to recall just how unsafe our early adventure had been. But for now it was utterly joyous. The orderly rows -- it seemed like miles upon miles of them -- of fruit trees cast brilliant shadows in the early evening, and the whole world smelled as sweet as a produce store.

And then, finally, Wenatchee presented itself. Even in those days -- especially in those days -- Wenatchee was the jewel of central Washington. Its splendid geographic location meant a climate perfectly suited to orchard crops, and its quality and variety of tree fruits were the envy of the world. Being the eastern station for changing train engines also gave Wenatchee a commercial flavor, and we admired the great expanse of the rail yard. We could hardly wait for the train to slow up enough for us to jump off and rest our weary palms. We could light up some smokes and laugh and regroup. Wenatchee by early evening seemed to be just about everything four young adventurers could ask for -- except for the one conspicuous thing that it wasn't: it wasn't Ellensburg, not even close.

"Yeah," Benjamin was saying as we strolled through the railroad yard, trying to look as though we belonged there. "I guess it kind of occurred to me up toward Peshastin. I looked around and realized we weren't gonna be making any turns up toward Blewett Pass.''

"Well," Tackett demanded, "then why didn't ya say something?''

I intervened. "I think," I said, as diplomatically as possible, "that what Ron means is that when he realized we weren't headed toward Ellensburg it didn't make a whole lot of difference. Because by then we were barrelin' down at about 30 miles an hour, and I don't think it would've been real advisable to jump off.''

"And even if we had jumped off," Duane noted, rubbing his sore hands together and making a few phantom golf-club swings, "what good would it have done? We'd still be stuck by the side of the railroad tracks, only it'd be back in Peshastin instead of here in the apple capital of the world.''

"But," Tackett argued, "there has to be other trains out of Peshastin.''

"Nah, there's the Northern Pacific that runs over Snoqualmie Pass to Ellensburg," Benjamin said. "Nothin' over Blewett.''

"It doesn't make much difference now, I guess," I said. "We're still a long ways from Ellensburg.''

By then it was growing dark. If we'd been able to keep to our expected schedule, we'd long since have gotten to Ellensburg. When I thought about the events of the recent 24 hours, it was dificult to imagine how much had come and gone. From a kind of pipe dream about Ellensburg, we'd actually planned the trip and set out. Then, just as everything was going better than expected, the car gets impounded and we're back on the bottom again. Life sure had its ups and downs. Being boys, we knew that anyway. But seldom had matters gone from good to bad to good to bad, from high to low and back again as they had during the past 24 hours.

"I guess it's back to thumbing a ride," Tackett finally said, daring to speak the words everybody else sensed were true, but none of us wanted to admit.

"Have to split up, then," Duane groused. "That's the last thing in the world I wanted to do."

"Same here," Benjamin said. "Scary as that tunnel ride was, it was a lot more fun than standing by the side of the road with your thumb stuck out."

"It was scary, all right," Tackett agreed, "but I'd take it over flopping around in the back of some farmer's flatbed truck anytime."

I felt bad for the other boys. I wasn't even sure at the time where to look for Ellensburg in relationship to Wenatchee, but I knew it was way out of the way from where we were.

"What about it, Ron?" I asked Benjamin. "What's the easiest way down to Ellensburg from here, just follow the Columbia south?"

Benjamin had a pretty fair sense of where we were.

"The problem," he said, "is that there isn't any real good way down there. It's like we're on a clock face. We're at about 1 o'clock and Ellensburg's back around at about 7 o'clock."

"Meanwhile," Tackett said, "it's getting on toward 8 o'clock right here, and it ain't gettin' any earlier, either."

But Benjamin ignored him and continued. "Back to Peshastin by train, then over Blewett along 97: That's one way."

"That'd mean thumbing through Blewett," Duane concluded.

"Assuming," Tackett noted, "we'd be able to jump off the train in Peshastin."

"The other way," Benjamin said, "is to try to hitch south, but that'd mean heading east a ways, then backtracking. And the roads have gotta be lousy, 'least that's what I remember from comin' back from Idaho.''

Then it dawned on me. When Benjamin said Idaho I blurted out:

''Ron, you've got relatives in Idaho, right?''

''Sandpoint, yeah,'' he said, ''why?''

I didn't say anything right away. Instead I looked back and forth at each of the boys, staring into their eyes the way I had back in Skykomish. I had the new idea fully formed already. It was outrageous -- the most fantastic thing I'd ever dreamed of doing. But I didn't dare present it to them right away because I wasn't even sure whether I myself had the nerve to utter the plan. So I started out by working the long way around.

''Seems to me,'' I said, ''that we need to look at our options here.''

Tackett lit a smoke and sat down in the dust, and the other two boys leaned against an old track buffer we'd come to at the far end of the yard.

''We set out all along to get to Ellensburg,'' I noted, ''but why?''

''Because it was your bright idea,'' Tackett laughed, and I threw my spent match at him and continued.

''To work and get some money: That was one reason,'' I said.

''The main reason,'' Benjamin said.

''Not really,'' I countered. ''The main reason was because there was nothing to do back in Seattle. We were just looking for something fun to do.''

''And we sure found it,'' Duane interrupted.

But then everybody paused, because at that instant we all understood something: Duane had spoken the exact truth of the matter. We had indeed found something fun to do, and each of us in our own way knew it.

"Oh," I said, "I suppose we could thumb our way back up and around Peshastin and down over Blewett. Then, when we finished working over there, we could all split up and thumb home to Seattle. It's possible."

The boys all looked down into the dust.

"It's also possible," I said, "that we could just stay here in Wenatchee a few days, maybe head up toward Chelan and work the orchards right here. That way we could hop a freight home when we were through. It would beat having to split up and hitchhike."

"I'm sure for that," Duane smiled.

"And then," I added, "since we now know how to catch trains and ride them for free, we could always just walk across the yard, catch one westbound and maybe be back in Seattle by morning."

Silence reigned. I knew none of the boys wanted to go home with tails between our legs. Oh, sure, our parents probably wouldn't care one way or the other. Gay Tackett might give Benjamin a hard time, and Mr. Benjamin would have to be dealt with sooner rather than later. But going home would mean returning to those long days of lying about waiting for something to happen, knowing nothing ever would. It would mean resigning ourselves to precisely the summertime boredom that had prompted the trip to begin with. And I for one would've done just about anything to prevent that from happening.

"How much money we got?" I finally asked.

We didn't have much. The little bit of shopping we'd done in Skykomish had claimed more than a dollar, so we probably couldn't scrape up three bucks between us.

"Money for what?" Tackett demanded.

"Well," I said, "cigarettes, for one thing. Maybe some

bread and lunch meat. We can pick fruit if we get too hungry.''

Benjamin perked up. ''Too hungry doing what?'' he wanted to know.

''Too hungry aboard the train,'' I smiled, looking each of them in the eye. ''Because here's my idea.''

I knew it was a risk to suggest it, because I could just hear them say a resounding ''no.'' But the time had come to say what was on my mind.

''Duane and me,'' I said, ''you know our dad. Well, he lives in DeLamere, which is in North Dakota.''

Duane still didn't sense where I was going with this, but he gamely volunteered: ''That's near Breckenridge.''

''Breckenridge, Minnesota?'' Tackett said.

''That's right,'' I said, then I clammed up for a few seconds.

''So what's that got to do with us?'' Benjamin asked, innocently.

''Well,'' I said, trying to be as persuasive as possible, ''I've got a feeling that since it only took about an hour to get down to Wenatchee from Skykomish, then I bet it wouldn't take more than two days for a train to make it back to Breckenridge.''

Finally Duane caught the gist. ''Go all the way back on the train to Dad's place?''

''You're crazy,'' Tackett laughed. ''That's half way across the darned country, Jerry. That ain't no day trip over the Cascades.''

But Benjamin liked the idea, even though he didn't say anything right away.

''Look,'' I said, ''what if we could get aboard a boxcar or a flatcar, so we'd be riding in comfort without having to cling to ladders like canaries?''

"I kind of like the clinging part," Duane said.

"But Jerry," Benjamin finally said, "it's a long ways."

"Not by train it isn't," I said, with nothing in my experience to justify such confidence. Then I hastily added: "The other thing is, once we got to North Dakota we could pick spuds there. They grow some of the best red potatoes in the world back there."

"Well," Duane said, "you can count me in. I'll go for sure."

I searched Benjamin's face. Of the four of us, he'd been through the most trauma, what with the car and the leaving his girlfriend in Seattle and the anxiety about his dad and all. If he'd nixed the idea I'd sure have understood.

But suddenly he started to grin a little. He ran a hand through his thick mop of hair and said: "We'd go through Sandpoint, wouldn't we? I've still got relatives there."

Tackett was the last to speak. "Since I'm youngest," he sighed, "I guess my vote doesn't count. But you know what I think?"

I was afraid of what he'd say, but the little guy surprised me.

"I think," he smiled, "we'd better get aboard and get bedded down before the train leaves."

Chapter 7

I don't think a single one of us ever asked ourselves at that moment: "What will our parents think of this turn of events? What would Mom and Dad say if they knew we'd decided on a lark to just forget about the Ellensburg end of the plan and pack off half way across the country?" It wasn't like that in those days. Oh, sure: We were disciplined by our parents and we had respect for them. But they didn't fret and fuss over us nearly so much as folks sometimes do today.

What we really had done was trade one potential adventure for another one of much broader consequences. The discovery of the railroad was the reason. Riding that train up out of Skykomish, being greeted by that harrowing looking WPA-style portal at the west end of the forbidding Cascade Tunnel, surviving the dark ride underground -- it was all as though we'd been given this wondrous Christmas toy. Then, when it appeared we'd have to give it back an hour later in Wenatchee . . . well, I think it was more than any of us could bear to imagine.

Not that Wenatchee itself wasn't an extraordinary place to be. The freight yards there were nicknamed "Apple Yard," for obvious reasons. Freight cars full of boxes of apples and other fruit were loaded on small sidings near each apple-packing plant, then moved to Apple Yard for shipment to whatever destination was desired. The museums in the valley attest today to the unsurpassed variety of apples produced over the decades in that part of the world. In 1948 there were a lot more independent growers than there are now, and each of them had individual brand identities and labels. Maybe ''Apple World'' would've been the better nickname for that freight yard.

Wenatchee also was the connection point of one of the Great Northern's largest branch lines in the state of Washington. The line extended north along the Columbia River into British Columbia and all the way west to Vancouver, B.C. Since much of this branch-line expanse was apple-producing country, Apple Yard was a very busy place this time of year.

We had no idea how long the train would be here. We knew they needed to switch engines from electric to steam or diesel, but other than that our railroad knowledge began and ended with being veteran stowaways.

The object, now that we'd decided to continue east, was to make sure we had all our gear together so that we could get aboard when the opportunity arose. We knew we couldn't travel much farther on ladders or couplings. The ideal would be to find the relatively cushy accommodations of a boxcar -- preferrably an empty one. That way we'd be able to sprawl out or stand around, and we'd have open views from either side. Unfortunately, we assumed, any empty boxcar in Apple Yard soon would be filled with produce before heading out.

A flatcar stacked with lumber maybe? It would give us just about everything we'd get from a boxcar, though safety wouldn't necessarily be part of the deal. On the other hand, what did any of us really know about riding the rails? We'd only been at it for about an hour.

In any case, we walked across the yards as though we

owned the place. The experience was so new to us that we didn't know any better. Would it be better to run or hide? We didn't know, and nobody said anything to us, so in not much time we just figured we must've looked as though we belonged there -- like sneaking onto a golf course, only much more of an adventure for us.

After a while Tackett and Benjamin dashed off to a nearby orchard and filled up their pockets with fruit. It's amazing looking back years later to realize the close proximity of the open fields to the railroad yard. While Duane and I stayed back with the baggage and assessed the goings on at Apple Yard I came to a sudden appreciation of what it meant to have so much available to us for free. We could ride these trains forever if we could get away with it. The fruit? Much of it would drop as windfall and spoil anyway. Was there anything morally objectionable to what we were doing? You had to think about it in the context of what we'd just been through as a country. First there was the Great Depression, when Duane and I had come into our formative years. Everything was scarce then, especially money. If you could catch a ride or grab a piece of fruit off the ground, more power to you. And even with times as tough as they were, Duane and I still led a fairly sheltered childhood. When war came along, and with it the greatest crisis in history, we knew about it all mostly through radio and newspaper accounts. At home we knew everybody was pulling together, making do with what we had.

And so this was what we had just now: a great opportunity. And we were seizing it no matter what happened.

Tackett and Benjamin returned with a fine supply of apples, and the four of us waited for the trains to start moving. For the longest time nothing seemed to happen in the Apple Yard. Pretty soon we grew restless, and I wondered whether this was a sign that maybe we were better off scrapping our plans.

"What's taking so long?" Duane asked no one in particular. "They switched engines a long time ago. They're just sittin' around the yard now, wasting time."

Then it became apparent what was causing the delay. A luxurious Empire Builder came cruising in from the east. It was the sleekest looking thing I'd seen in a while -- certainly much classier looking than any freight. In those days the Empire Builder passenger cars were being redesigned, with the old emphasis on East Coast-style luxury shifting to a more Western design scheme with Indian influences. From where we were waiting it was impossible to tell whether the passenger cars were of the new or older design. We marveled, though, and Tackett sighed:

"Now that's what I call riding in style."

"Wait 'til you see the car we catch," I assured him.

But it was undeniable that I was curious about what it would be like amid the finery of one of those passenger cars. For the better part of a century the railroads had provided the ultimate in luxury transportation. We had no way of knowing in 1948 that the days were numbered for this venerable mode of travel, though signs of it were everywhere. The Mercer Island Bridge had opened during the early years of the war, and now motorists could drive between Seattle and points east without having to go around through Lake City and Bothell. Road construction was booming, and now that the auto plants were up and producing again after the lapse during the war years it should've seemed obvious to all that the family car soon would replace the train. When the interstate-highway system and mass air travel were introduced during the '50s, train service gradually cut back to the point where it's nothing now compared with 1948.

But the Apple Yard activity ceased in deference to the Empire Builder. Then, when the passenger train was outfitted with its electric engine and sent chugging toward the tunnel (through which U.S. presidents had passed by train), we noted that the yard activity was alive once more. My brief rhapsody about passenger cars came to an end with the realization that a golden opportunity was about to pass before us. It was a boxcar, all right. More to the point: Its door was wide open. That meant we could board with relative ease -- assuming we timed it right.

"What we need to remember," I said, "is that there isn't going to be anything easy to grab hold of like there was last time. That means we'll have to throw our stuff up there and hop on while the train's still going slow enough for us."

The train continued its slow, certain progression eastward, and we moved toward the tracks. As the open boxcar approached we began jogging in place, then jogging along the same direction as the train.

"Nobody watching?" Benjamin shouted above the steely screeching of the train wheels.

"I don't think so," I yelled. "C'mon. It's time."

As the boxcar passed before us we tossed the grip through the wide door and onto the rough wooden floor.

"Tackett, climb on!" I yelled, and in a second he was aboard.

Then went Benjamin, who turned and grabbed Duane's shirt as my brother agilely got on. Now the train was picking up speed, but I knew I could swing up without much problem. We were losing our light in the late summer night, and I was troubled for a second for not having anything to grab. I banged my elbows a little scrambing aboard, then looked back as the Apple Yard seemed to fall away from us in the distance. There was no going back now, and we all seemed to know it. We gradually got up from our sprawl and looked around the new environment apprehensively. Then Duane broke the stillness.

''Next stop, DeLamere!'' he shouted, and the four of us laughed with delight.

It's nearly impossible to describe the exhilaration we felt, standing on the swaying floor of the enclosed boxcar, the country air flying by the door as night fell. The train coursed down south along the west side of the wide Columbia, continuing this way for about 10 miles before abruptly turning and taking the rail bridge across.

>Oh, you'll never get to heaven
>>(Oh, you'll never get to heaven)
>In a rockin' chair.
>>(In a rockin' chair).
>'Cause the Lord don't allow
>>('Cause the Lord don't allow)
>No lazy folks there.
>>(No lazy folks there).

>Oh, yes you'll never get to heaven
>>In a rockin' chair.
>'Cause the Lord don't allow
>>No lazy folks there.

>I ain't gonna grieve, my Lord no more.
>I ain't gonna grieve, my Lord no more.
>I ain't gonna grieve, my Lord no more.
>I ain't gonna grie-e-e-ve, my Lord no more.

As the train passed above the gorge we could see for

miles as we headed east. Passing through Quincy and Odessa, we could see even by night that the country was growing desolate in a way that can make parts of Eastern Washington by night look barren as the surface of the moon. It was like a dark desert, with scents of sage but without any desert monuments such as the cactus you see in the Southwest. In some parts of such areas of Eastern Washington they could manage pretty good quality crop soil if there was water to be had. But that part of Washington is known for its intense winds. Lots of times the wind kicks up miniature tornadoes called "dust devils," and at any given time we could see a dozen or more of them dancing in the distance. Every plot of recently plowed land seemed to have one, with some of these devils rising up 100 feet.

It occurred to me that the sensation of standing in an open boxcar was unlike anything we'd experienced. It was like this: If you had a house with a big picture window and a magnificent view, then you could stand a few feet back with the drapes open and see the panorama before you. In a boxcar with open doors we had that same panoramic view, but the view kept changing. It was as though we were seeing the whole world passing by in cinemascope.

So it wasn't as though we merely got to see these enormous dust devils. The sensation was one of watching them dance like untethered marionettes in the distance. They would twist and twirl across a piece of plowed ground, only to disappear when coming to a plot of unplowed ground, in turn reappearing where the plowing recommenced. Is that where the expression "devil's dance" comes from? I don't know, but having seen it that night, eerie in the near distance, I can sure make a case for it.

But the long day finally was coming to an end. If anyone had told me that morning that, instead of camping next to a car in Ellensburg, we'd actually be on an eastbound freight headed who knew where, I'd have sworn they were crazy.

No wonder we were weary. Even boys in their high-energy teen years can suffer from stress, and on that day we had plenty of it. There had been the tremendous emotional stress -- the ups and downs in Seattle and Skykomish, through the tunnel and on to Wenatchee and beyond. And then there had been the physical activity: running for trains, shouldering our grip, hanging on for dear life to boxcar-ladder rungs.

So it was a relief when we finally rolled out our bedding and gradually started to yield to slumber. I'm not sure of what was going through the minds of the others that night as the train cadence slowly lulled us toward sleep. But my own mind was full of doubts. That brief period just prior to sleep had always been my time to question my own actions and motives. Sure: No harm had come to us, other than the wounded pride of having lost the car. But none of us had lost any other material possessions, and each of us remained in good health. More important: Our spirits were as high as they'd ever been.

Still, I was the oldest of the group and the obvious leader. If anything bad should happen, the others easily could rationalize what they'd done by saying they were just going along with the gang. Not me. Not only would I have to own up to the consequences. It also would be on my conscience if any real harm came to the others.

So it was with mixed emotions that I finally gave way and shut my eyes. One day had passed and we weren't even out of Washington yet -- not even half way across. Breckenridge was a long way away, and what lay ahead was so uncertain.

Chapter 8

$\mathcal{J}$t was barely dawn when we awoke the next morning, and the first thing I realized was that we weren't moving. The boxcar was still as a coffin. I could hear none of the telltale clickety-clack signifying wheels on rail joints. Nothing. Were we back home? Had the entire adventure of the previous day merely been a dream?

Gradually the boys came to consciousness. We yawned and stretched, and refamiliarized ourselves with our surroundings. The boxcar, because it was so well-ventilated, had kept us less than warm during the night. I was a little sore from the activities of the previous day, but I also was looking forward to seeing what the new day would bring. If it were to be even half as eventful as the previous day, then we were in for quite an adventure.

We got out of the car, taking our gear with us so that we wouldn't lose it on the train. But after investigating it occurred to us that this was about as far as our empty boxcar was going to go. We had come to the Great Northern Railroad's Hillyard yards in the northern outskirts of Spokane. The place was so-named because of its proximity to the suburb of Hillyard, and our car was on a siding adjacent to the neighborhood.

"I don't know about you guys," I said, "but I could use a warm place to plop down for a while."

They agreed, and we found what appeared to be an all-hours cafe nearby. This presented both a blessing and a problem. It was warm and well-lighted, and it had a cigarette machine. But it also caused us to reassess our financial situation. By now we were down to just a couple dollars, and with Breckenridge still three states away we were aware that there couldn't be any extravagant purchases.

"I'll have coffee," I said to the waitress at the counter.

"Milk for me," each of the others chimed in.

With one pack of smokes between us, we sipped and lingered as long as we thought management would allow. I for one was reluctant to get up and go out into the cool morning, but eventually we pulled ourselves up and wandered back toward the Hillyard yards. Our provisions were about shot. The apples from Wenatchee were long since devoured, and by midmorning there remained but a scant few smokes between us.

"At this rate," Tackett groused, "we'll never get where we're going."

It was nearly noon before an eastbound freight availed itself -- sort of. Unlike in Wenatchee, no cushy boxcar could be seen. Nor was there even a flatcar to climb on. So much for the Great Northern's accommodations, I thought.

"I guess we'll just have to do what we did in Skykomish," I concluded.

"Hey, that was fun," Duane grinned.

Fun in retrospect, maybe. For me, the preferred mode was an empty boxcar, but suddenly the train was picking up speed and it was time to jump aboard. We made sure our sleeping bags and bundles were securely tied so that we wouldn't lose them, and when the engine had passed us by several cars we dashed for the ladders.

Once aboard it occurred to me that I'd neglected to procure the one item I really wanted: a road map. As it was, we could only guess as to what the order of towns would be along the route. Benjamin, with relatives in Idaho, imagined that Sandpoint would be our next stop. Or maybe Bonner's Ferry. The rest of us had no clear idea of the geography ahead of us, other than the fact that the tracks led eventually to Breckenridge: The important thing was that we were on the freight and headed east.

At the same time, riding between boxcars was not the least bit comfortable, not even for grizzled one-day rail-riding veterans such as ourselves.

"I hate to complain," Tackett yelled, "but doesn't there have to be a better way to travel than this?"

So even though it would be a cumbersome effort we decided to climb and explore. Cinching up our bedrolls and belongings again, we climbed to the top of the rear boxcar. We'd already seen the front cars pass while waiting to board the train at Hillyard. We knew there was nothing available toward the front of the train, so we cautiously walked toward the rear.

What an odd sensation that was. The engine was pulling all the cars forward to the north, and here we were, gradually moving backward to the south. The afternoon breeze blew hot through our hair, and we could see the evidence of logging as we chugged along toward the northeast extremity of the state. In those days there was little evidence of anything else. Not much of the northern outskirts of Spokane had been settled by then, and Highway 2, which snaked along near the tracks for much of the way, was but a trickle of hard-rock road -- a seldom traveled route for farm trucks and pre-war-vintage autos.

The train was still moving at a relatively slow pace. There was a walkway on top, and with little swaying there wasn't much danger any of us would lose our footing and fall.

After walking back a distance of about 10 boxcars we were disappointed to find no better accommodations. From that vantage point we could see back another 20 cars or so, and still there appeared to be nothing approaching the relatively splendid ride we'd enjoyed the night before.

"I guess the ladders are the best we can do for now," I concluded, as we gradually climbed back down between boxcars. "I hope this train is stopping somewhere before Breckenridge, because if not we're in for some weary bones."

Looking back, maybe it would've been just as well if the train had gone nonstop to Breckenridge. Look out for what you wish for, I guess, because it may just come true.

And it did. Our mistake had been to climb to the top in the first place. Hidden between boxcars, we probably never would've been detected. But our little hike across the tops of the boxcars made us easily visible as we approached the rear of the train, where a brakeman on the caboose saw us taking our free rides.

We could only imagine the chain of events. Probably what happened was that the brakeman radioed up to the engineer and spilled the beans. Then the engineer probably signalled ahead to the authorities at what was to be the next stop on our adventure. In any event, our next stop came less than an hour from the time we'd left Hillyard, and by no means had we made it to Sandpoint or Bonner's Ferry -- or Idaho, for that matter.

Instead we were "greeted," if the word applies, by Newport, Washington. Newport was a remote but prosperous timber town that had been an important stop along the railroad line since the turn of the century. By 1948 it boasted a vibrant downtown area of stores and movie theaters -- none of which we were destined to enjoy. Instead, as the train pulled in along the Pend Oreille River across the water from Idaho, the most significant structure we could see was the City Hall building with a clock tower rising up above it two blocks toward town.

But the building wasn't the main attraction in the early afternoon at Newport. The main sight was a pair of uniformed policemen standing back from the yard, staring directly at us.

"Oh, my God, Jerry," Duane sighed, "we're really in trouble now."

Evidently he was right, as one of the cops beckoned us humorlessly, waving a hand and saying: "Come on, boys, you're coming with us."

I looked at the other three. They all looked pretty anxious, and I suppose I did, too. After our brush with the law the day before, I guess we figured we'd had our share of police contact. Benjamin looked at me as though to say: "Hey, weren't we just going to go to Ellensburg and pick crops? What's all this about?"

I took the cue and engaged the cops in conversation.

"Uh," I said, "what's the problem, officer?"

"Problem?" he repeated. "Didn't your folks ever tell you kids it's darned dangerous running and playing on top of freight trains? A kid'd get killed falling off from up there."

"Sorry, officer," I said, "but we were neither running or playing. We were just looking for a better place to ride."

For the life of me I thought my explanation sounded pretty innocent. After all, what harm were we causing the Great Northern Railroad? Between us we couldn't have weighed more than a quarter ton -- our belongings included. We weren't out to disturb anybody. We just needed a lift. But the cop wasn't hearing any of it. He motioned for us to throw our stuff into the trunk of a squad car and the four of us sandwiched into the back seat.

"See, boys," the other officer said. "The point is that you're not supposed to be riding up there -- period! These are modern times now. Boys like you oughta be home with their families, playing ball, having clean fun Riding the rails, that's for hoboes."

"But," I protested, "we're just trying to get back to Breckenridge, trying to see my dad. How else are we gonna get there?"

"I have no idea, boys," the second cop said. "But for now you're not going anywhere but jail."

Jail? In less than 48 hours we'd gone from lolling around the neighborhood in Seattle to a jail cell on the other side of the state?

Well, maybe not quite a cell. It was a holding area with bars on the bottom floor of the city hall building. But first we had to go through the processing procedure at the front desk.

"We'll need to get all your names and ages, addresses if you've got any," the first cop said. "You sure you're not running away from home?"

"Honest," I said. "My dad lives in DeLamere, North Dakota."

The second cop looked confused. "Thought you said Breckenridge."

"It's near there," Duane volunteered. "He's my dad, too."

The second cop said: "And you other two boys? You're just along for the ride, I suppose."

They said nothing. What could they say? If we'd explained exactly what had happened to us in two days the police probably would've been even more skeptical than they were now.

By the time the processing was finished and we'd been hauled into the holding area, my stomach was growling. It occurred to me that none of us had eaten anything more substantial than apples and candy bars since we left home.

My familiarity with jail routine was as limited as a lot of my other real-world experience, which is to say: I mainly knew the way things happened in the movies.

"Officer," I said before he left, "do you suppose the guys and I will be able to get lunch while we're in here?"

The cops seemed somewhat amused by this, saying: "You didn't think this was a restaurant, did you?"

"No," I said, "but I thought we were entitled to a meal in jail."

"You are," he said. "But lunch is served here at noon."

I glanced at my Timex: 12:30.

"Half an hour ago," I noted, still hopeful of getting a scrap of bread and bologna maybe.

"Very good," the cop cracked. "So you missed lunch by half an hour." The other three boys were as disheartened as I was.

"Then what about dinner?" Tackett demanded. "When's that?"

"Five o'clock," the cop said, locking us in. "Sharp."

In truth, I don't think the police had any idea what to do with us. Hopping freights probably wasn't something you charged someone for unless the railroad wanted to make an issue of it, and clearly the Great Northern had more important concerns than four Seattle kids climbing on boxcars.

Maybe they were just trying to teach us a lesson on this lazy summer afternoon. Whatever the case, they were making it difficult for us to pass the time, what with the hunger pangs growing by the hour.

The holding area was just a 12-by-12 room crowded with bunks, a table a few benchs and a bathroom stall. There was a well-used pack of playing cards on the table and a few old Life magazines. I soon found that I couldn't bear to look at the magazines because the food pictures made me even hungrier.

"I could eat flies right now, if I had the energy to swat them," Tackett said.

"Five o'clock," Duane mused. "That seems like forever right now."

It seemed even more of an eternity as the afternoon wore on. We'd slept reasonably well on the boxcar the night before, so none of us was much interested in resting on the ricketty steel-frame cots. Instead we passed the time shuffling and dealing the flimsy cards, playing endless rounds of rummy.

"How long can they hold us in here?" Duane asked at one point.

"Long as they want," Benjamin sighed. "They're the cops."

"But," Tackett protested, "don't they have to charge us with something?"

"Eventually," I suggested, "but I don't know when. Anyway, I'm not pressing the issue, because I want to stay here at least until 5 o'clock or I'm going to starve to death."

By 3:30 we were bored stiff with rummy. Pacing in the cell, we seemed to check our wristwatches about twice a minute.

"I haven't seen time pass like this since the last day of school," Tackett groaned.

At 4:30 there seemed to be some activity in the police office.

"They're probably sending out for food now," Duane

speculated. "I doubt if they've got cooking facilities here."

Nothing happened for a couple more long minutes. Then my heart raced as the cop appeared at the door. Finally, I thought. A big, juicy hamburger maybe, or even a scrap of stale bread. Wasn't that what you got in jail? Stale bread? I'd take it.

It was the first officer. The other either was off duty by now or was off fetching our meal.

"Okay, boys," the cop said, throwing the door open. "C'mon."

We looked at one another in disbelief.

"C'mon where?" I asked, tentatively.

"I'm releasing you," he said. "Let's go."

I made a great spectacle of looking at my wristwatch.

"But," I argued, "we haven't had our meal yet. It's not 5 o'clock."

"Smart kid," the cop deadpanned. "And I hope you boys will be smart enough from now on not to let anybody catch you hopping trains -- not in Newport, anyway."

"What are you going to do with us?" I demanded.

The cop looked me up and down. "That's your choice," he finally said. "I'll drive you to the city limits, but you've got to decide which end of town. All I know is that whichever end it is, I don't want to see any of you back in Newport again. Hear me?"

I was almost too hungry to think straight. What a dirty deal this was: holding us between the lunch and dinner hours and then not feeding us. But the cops could get away with it: That much I understood only too well. Now it was left to me to make another fateful decision: Were we still heading east or were we turning our tails back home?

But the decision was taken out of my hands when the other three said more or less in unison: "East."

The officer checked us back our belongings and had us pile into the car. He drove us to the east end of the bridge over the Pend Oreille where, technically, we were in Idaho.

"I feel duty bound to remind you kids," the cop said. "We don't want to see you back here in Newport. We catch you hanging around the rail yards and it'll be hard on you. I promise. And we'll be watching, too."

Chapter 9

$\mathcal{J}$ guess there are degrees of hunger. Nobody can say they're starving to death when they've had something to eat within the past day. On the other hand, we were teenage boys used to eating great quantities of food. We'd also expended lots of energy during this adventure. But still the hunger would've been far less difficult to handle if we hadn't spent the entire afternoon anticipating 5 p.m., imagining the meal that it would bring. That's the worst kind of hunger: when you're ready to eat, planning to eat, hoping to eat, dying to eat, but the meal doesn't come.

Or, even worse, suddenly you're told that the meal never IS going to come. Instead, here we were in Idaho, with little money, no smokes and no easy access to the railroad. The officer had made it dreadfully clear of what we could expect if we chanced back into town. He seemed to make it his personal challenge to see to it we never stepped foot again in Newport, Washington.

I scarcely needed to appraise our predicament for the boys. They knew as well as I did that we were in a dire situation. Our only possible prospect now was to try to hitch a ride on a truck or, less likely, in a car. There was a large sawmill up the road at Priest River, but it wasn't generating much auto traffic. So we weren't really any better off than we would've been trying to thumb from Wenatchee down to Ellensburg.

But I sensed everybody now wondered whether we wouldn't have been better sticking with the original plan instead of taking this extreme departure across the country. We'd gone not much more than 300 miles. That meant there remained some 1,200 miles to travel before we'd get to DeLamere.

I don't know whether the boys were too brave or proud -- or maybe just too punchy -- to protest, but I had to hand it to them. No one dissented, even after all we'd been through. We seemed to agree implicitly that, for better or worse, this was the right course.

And what a course! Highway 2 east out of Newport continued to snake along with the wide Pend Oreille. But aside from the lumber mill off to the south, about all we could see was an occasional farm house set well back from the roads. Dogs would bay in the distance, and as we trudged along Highway 2 I suddenly knew the true meaning of the song phrase "look down, look down that lonesome road."

"Is There really any point walking?" Benjamin wondered after we'd scuffed along the dusty road for half a mile. "I mean, we can't walk all the way back to DeLamere, can we?"

He had a point. On the other hand, it felt as though we were at least making forward progress if we walked instead of stood. And after the experience in Newport I didn't feel like lingering near the city limit if we didn't have to. Frankly, I didn't care if I ever saw Newport again.

The other point about walking had to do with strategy. Hitchhiking had been common in those days, and it remained popular (mostly among young, otherwise immobile, men) through the 1960s, until the growing threat of violence made it too dangerous to pick up hitchhikers. We learned that drivers were more likely to stop for us if we appeared to be making an effort to get somewhere on our own two feet instead of remaining stationary and looking lazy.

So even though we felt starved, we gamely pushed on -- for a while. After about three miles I could stand it no longer. We came to a farm house that sat a quarter mile up north of Highway 2. On one side a few cows grazed in a pasture. It was a picture of amity that suggested maybe I could have some luck if I tried.

''I'm starving,'' I said to the others. ''And I'm just hungry enough to go up to that place and see if I can do something to get a bite to eat.''

We talked it over and decided it would be better if I indeed went alone. If we all went it might look a little threatening to the residents, and we sure didn't need anymore scrapes with the law.

I cautiously walked up the long gravel driveway to where the yard met the house. An old dog shuffled around the house and past a pickup truck, crowing once before nervously coming over to sniff the stranger.

''Here goes nothing,'' I said to myself, and I rapped on the door.

It took a minute, but finally a balding man with brushy eyebrows wearing a flannel shirt and overalls appeared at the door.

''Pard' me, sir,'' I began, tentatively. ''But I don't suppose there's anything I could do around here to earn a bite to eat, is there?

There was a long silence, and I was getting nervous. This had been a bad idea, I decided, and I almost blurted out an apology when the man suddenly looked past me down toward the road and asked:

"Those your buddies down there?"

"Well, yes sir," I said. "Y'see, we're on our way back to North Dakota to see my dad. The one boy's my brother. The other two are our friends."

The farmer sized me up, then said to himself "hmmm. .." Then he started to turn away from the door and my heart sank.

"Wait here a minute, son," he said, giving me a little hope. "I'll be right back."

What, I wondered, did this mean? Was he calling the cops? Probably not in Newport, though, because even if it was only three miles down the road it was in another state.

Finally he returned to the door, but this time he was smiling faintly.

"Wave your buddies up here," he said, "then come on into the kitchen."

I don't think I ever saw the other three run any faster. With the belongings flopping every which way, they were a blur coming up that driveway as the sun slid in behind the high pines near St. Regis.

"Jerry, what's up?" Duane panted.

"Don't know for sure," I half-whispered, "but you guys leave the stuff out here and let's go in."

We stood awkwardly in the dimly lit living room for a moment. Then we heard a booming voice from the kitchen yelling: "C'mon into the kitchen boys."

We were amazed at what we saw. In the center of the large, immaculate farmhouse kitchen was a large, round oak table set with four places. Each place setting had an empty white plate, a napkin and a tall glass by the side. In the middle of the table was a pitcher of milk and a plate heaped high with sandwiches: ham sandwiches, cheese, ham-and-cheese. One good whiff was all that was needed to tell me that the home-made bread the sandwiches were made with was just recently out of the oven. There is just something about the aroma of home made bread that seems to hang in the air for hours after the oven is turned off. And, oh boy, did it smell good. It was such a welcome spectacle that we only secondarily noticed someone standing at the far end of the kitchen.

"My daughter, Alice," the farmer said proudly. "My name's Murphy. Everyone just calls me Murph. My Wife's down to Cour D'Alene visiting an ailing sister. Sit down boys, sit down. Dig in boys. I like to see boys eat hearty."

Mr. Murphy had a real gruff sounding voice but it had a friendly quality to it that more than compensated for the gruffness.

As famished as we were we endeavored to use our best manners. Had the Murphy's not been standing before us we might easily have stuffed ourselves like animals.

"So," Murphy finally said after we'd started eating, "you say you boys are off to North Dakota to see your father."

"Ah, just my father and Duane's father, sir," I said. "We figure to work in the fields in harvest time for a while before heading back for Seattle. We figured to kill two birds with one stone on this trip. We hadn't seen dad in a while and we were looking for some summer work."

"You boys are kinda young to be travelling so far. Are you hitch hiking all the way?"

I suddenly realized that he probably got that impression because we had been out on the road so I started to tell him about the whole trip.

He had encouraged us to dig in to the food as soon as we sat down so I related the story as we ate. I would talk for a while, then take a couple of bites, and one of the others would take over.

We told him about starting out in the car, then, when they took it away from us, the decision to hop a freight and finally the decision to just keep going.

As we talked I could see that he was getting enthused and smiling and laughing more as we related our story. I also noted that Alice was smiling and laughing more, especially when it was Benjamin's turn to take over the story telling.

Alice was a very pretty girl with blue eyes and long blonde pigtails. She looked to be about 16 years old and she definitely seemed to be directing those blue eyes in Benjamins direction the majority of the time. A fact that did not go unnoticed by Gay Tacketts younger brother.

It didn't surprise me. The girls always went for Benjamin. Here he was: the only member of the group with a steady girlfriend, but he was still the one Alice found most interesting.

Farmer Murphy seemed truly entertained. I wasn't sure how vivid to make the details, but after a while I decided it wouldn't offend the Murphys to hear the whole truth. So I related the tale about the Newport jail.

"Well," the farmer said upon hearing about Newport, "it doesn't surprise me. Reminds me, in fact, of some of the adventures I had when I was about you boys' age."

I guess maybe it was fitting that the fee for our delicious meals would be the lending of our ears to Murphy's own stories.

And they were abundant. He told of the time that he and some young friends in Duluth had taken their canoes up through the northern waterways, eventually getting caught in ice and snow, and having to abandon their vessels and hike home half frozen.

"But I've also had a little experience on the freight trains," Murphy added. "When I was you boys' age there just wasn't much automobile traffic, and if you grew up out here in the west about the only way for a boy to get from one town to the next was to ride the rail. Times are changin' now, though. I'm kind of surprised four boys like yourselves have the initiative to set out like this. It's good to see."

"Good?" I repeated in my head. This was the first time since we'd left Skykomish that anybody besides the four of us had said anything positive about what we were doing. The police in Skykomish, impounding the car, had treated us like borderline criminals. Same with the cops in Newport. Now, suddenly, here was this father-figure actually approving of what we were doing.

The combination of the approval, the food and the presence of Alice's beauty put a glow on the evening. Alice kept making more sandwiches until we couldn't eat anymore, then quietly stood at a kitchen counter packing more food into a large brown shopping bag. She seemed delighted with our stories, which gradually went beyond the adventure and back to Seattle where we came from. It occurred to me that Seattle was the biggest city in the region, and it must've seemed awfully romantic and glamorous in the mind of this rural girl. For brief spells during the evening I found myself wishing I were back home. Then it would occur to me again that the adventure was what was making my past and present life seem so valuable and worth living, and I was glad once again that we'd taken this chance. I was particularly heartened by the fact that we hadn't given up back in Newport, when it might've been so easy to do so. If we had, then we never would've met these nice people, whose generosity restored our faith in strangers.

Then again, we seemed to be giving back our share to the

hosts. I imagined that was part of our "payment" for the Murphys' generosity. For the meal, they also were getting a chance encounter with strangers they found to be very entertaining. And the more we talked, the more Alice herself opened up, telling us about the things the local kids did for fun, about how all of them seemed to want to get out of Priest River some day and head for the bigger towns and cities.

At one point Benjamin asked whether he could excuse himself to the bathroom. Alice didn't hesitate for a second, putting aside her kitchen utensils and hastening to say:

"C'mon, Ron, I'll show you where it is."

Tackett rolled his eyes as Benjamin and Alice disappeared out of the kitchen, chatting their way down the hall. Farmer Murphy continued trading stories with us. In time we all used the bathroom, then checked our watches. Somehow we'd talked and visited right through to nightfall. Farmer Murphy suggested we could stay and sleep in the barn if we wanted, but I told him we'd imposed enough as it was. Alice planted a package of ginger snaps in with the sandwiches and we headed for the front yard.

"Tell you what, boys," Murphy proposed. "It's getting late out. Why don't I drive you back to Newport? You can't very well hitchhike, because you'll never get a ride unless you split up."

"That's the last thing we want, Mr. Murphy," Duane said.

"I'll take you back, then and show you where to try your luck with the trains again."

"Gee," I said, "that's great of you, but the cops will run us in if they see us."

"Well," Murphy laughed, "then we'll see to it they don't see you."

We started to climb into the back of the pickup. Alice

looked at us wistfully from across the yard, then suddenly yelled: ''Wait.''

She ran into the house for a minute, then came back with a folded piece of paper. She ran toward us and said:

''Now you've got to be sure and write to us, and tell us how it all came out.''

But I gathered what she meant by ''you'' was Ron Benjamin, because it was his hand that she squeezed the paper into -- a gesture that didn't escape the watchful eye of Gay Tackett's younger brother.

Nothing had ever been mentioned by any one about the sack of sandwiches that Alice had worked so hard at filling. Now as I hopped into the front seat with Mr. Murphy he placed the bag between us. Still not mentioning it.

Pretty soon we got to the east end of the bridge, and Murphy cut the truck lights so that we could behold Newport once more.

''I don't know about this,'' I said.

''Don't worry,'' Murphy said. ''The trick is to get down between the yard and the river. That way you can see when the trains move, but you can't be detected from up in town.''

As I got out of the cab he handed me the sack of sandwiches and said, ''here, take this. It isn't much but it'll hold you for a little while.''

With that the four of us vigorously shook hands with Murphy and crept off toward the train yard. We'd gotten a ways away when I looked back and saw that he was beckoning me to come back to the truck. What could he possibly want? I wondered. But I left my bundle with the other boys and scampered back.

''I almost forgot,'' Murphy smiled, reaching toward my shirt pocket. ''Here,'' he said, and he stuffed something inside. ''Now you boys be sure and be careful, you hear me?''

I didn't know quite what to do, so I thanked him kindly again and headed back.

''What was that all about?'' Tackett wanted to know.

Though I had not actually seen what he had stuffed into my shirt pocket I knew what it was. I just didn't know the denomination. I hadn't said anything to Mr. Murphy because I felt that if he had wanted me to say something he would have just handed it to me rather than stuffing it in my pocket.

So I made a big thing of being surprised. ''Well,'' I said, fishing into my pocket, ''let's see.''

''It was about Abe Lincoln, is what it was about,'' I laughed, showing around the five-dollar bill. ''Boys! We're rich!''

Chapter 10

*A*ll right, so maybe "rich" isn't quite right. On the other hand, five dollars had gotten us from Seattle to Newport. Now, with the sandwiches and cookies to sustain us, the money would help pay for our smokes and provide a buffer when the food ran out. If we kept living by our wits, who knows how far we could get?

And who knew what waited around the next bend? The adventure had been equal measures of highs and lows so far. Like life itself, our ups and downs had made us bewildered at one moment, elated at the next.

But I guess there was no denying that this was about as high as our spirits had soared.

"What did we do to deserve the Murphys?" Tackett asked rhetorically.

"We must be living right," Benjamin said, and we all laughed.

After we'd had a good chuckle and congratulated our-selves on our great fortune, I reminded the boys that another item remained on the evening's agenda.

"I'm not saying we necessarily have to catch a train out of here tonight," I suggested, "but this much I know: We need a few packs of smokes. One of us will need to sneak into town and get them.''

We looked back and forth at one another. Being the nominal leader, I knew I was silently nominated so I figured I might as well ''volunteer.'' It wasn't something I was looking forward to. That officer had made it awfully clear of the consequences if any of us was seen in Newport again, and this bothered me. After all, what had we really done that was so wrong? We obviously weren't juvenile delinquents. We'd explained to the police that we were just trying to get back to DeLamere. But I guess the cops had to be concerned about strangers in town, especially in a little out-of-the-way place like Newport. Maybe that was an advantage of living in a big city. In Seattle you could come and go without raising any suspicion. Now here I was: At night in a strange town, where one wrong move could land me in jail for longer than just an afternoon.

The boys had settled between the trains and the river, downstream a ways from town. We knew that the farther away we got the less likely it was that we'd be detected.

I needed only to get a couple of blocks into town in order to find a store that sold cigarettes. To reach the main drag meant having to pass in the proximity of Second Avenue and Washington Street, where the courthouse building sat in the moonlight, its roof buttressed and its belltower jutting into the sky. The place looked a little spooky at night, even though around the back I could see a faint light coming from the police station. I couldn't tell as I walked nearby whether any other unfortunates had wound up in the pokey that night, though I could sure bet they weren't getting fed if they had. Just as I came the nearest I needed to get to the courthouse I could see the same police car that had escorted us in and out of town earlier in the day. The car was pulling up Washington Street and heading into the main part of town.

Just my luck, I thought. Now I'll have to play cat-and-mouse with the cops just to get a few packs of smokes for us. Maybe this wasn't worth it after all. Did I really want to risk a run-in with either of those cops if only so the boys and I could have a few packs of cigarettes?

On the other hand, the attitude toward tobacco was much different back in 1948. Back then, before health commissions and surgeon-generals' reports, it seemed as though most everybody smoked. In fact, about 40 percent of the adult population did use tobacco during the late '40s, compared with only half that percentage now. A lot of kids our age smoked. Nobody really thought it was a big deal. Oh, sure: Your parents never really let on that it was okay, what with some kids getting promised a gold watch if they kept from smoking until they were 21. But I guess it was just sort of assumed that everybody eventually would smoke. It was glamorized in the movies. Sports figures even appeared in cigarette advertisements.

So the answer that night was a resounding: yes! It was well worth the risk of skulking into town, because we were out of smokes.

Fortunately that night the street activity in Newport was pretty lively. One of the movie theaters had just let out and folks were finding their ways to their homes or to the cafes that were still open. I guess I blended in pretty easily, as I ducked into a mom-and-pop grocery up Washington Street and ordered four packs of Luckies and as many Hershey bars. Turning to leave, though, I warily glanced out the window first. It was a good thing I did, too, because parked just across the street was Officer Number Two. Not only that, but it didn't appear he was moving.

Did I dare bolt out the front door? By now the pedestrian traffic had subsided quite a bit. If I'd had a hat to pull down over my eyes, then I might've been able to slouch down the street somewhat disguised. But I had no hat. Moreover, I figured the cop probably knew everybody in Newport, so he'd probably know I was a stranger even if he didn't catch sight of me until after I was a block away.

I checked my watch. It was nearly 9 o'clock now, so I figured the store would have to be closing. What to do? I glanced back nervously at the store clerk, an older man who seemed to regard me suspiciously.

"Anything else I can do for you, son?" the clerk finally asked.

I had to think. Should I buy time by browsing and maybe making another purchase? No, because the five bucks would only stretch so far. If only I'd waited to buy the candy bars.

"I'm trying to think if there's anything else I need," I said, stalling and looking back outside.

But the squad car was still there. And now the streets were devoid of foot traffic. The cop would spot me for sure if I walked out. Suddenly I felt like John Dillinger on the run.

Then it came to me.

"Say, Mister," I asked, hopefully, "you wouldn't happen to have a restroom out back, would you? I don't know if I can make it all the way to the filling station."

It was a desperate decision. If the clerk said "no" I'd have to either spend more money, bolt out the front and make a run for it or dash out the back. If I went out the front the cop would see me and follow me back to where the boys were camped. If I went the back route, the clerk might alert the officer anyway.

The older man sized me up.

"Well," he finally said, "it's just an outhouse, but it's back through the alley."

He motioned me to the rear of the store. Back behind

some produce boxes I found a wooden push door with a hook latch. I unhooked it, thanked the clerk and stepped out into the starry night, free -- for the moment. I knew it wouldn't do to go back to Washington Street. By now the cop might've moved. If he was patrolling, then I still could bump into him. The only reasonable option was to walk in a direction away from the river, up the hill toward the residences, then take a wide sweep around the outskirts of town and back down by the river. All this, I thought, for a few packs of smokes.

It was an odd sensation sneaking around like this. I felt a little like old Huck Finn, coming and going through town in the dark of night, dodging the authorities even though I'd still really done nothing wrong. But I figured that this was what the world was like: a place that demanded boys sneak around a little to get what they wanted and where they were going.

Within 15 minutes I'd managed to make my way around town and back down by the river. I wondered whether I'd even be able to find the boys in the dark, but they'd taken care of that for me. They'd gathered some scrap wood and built a small fire near the river. The fire might've been a little risky, given the need to stay out of the way of the cops. But we also needed light, not to mention the cheer the little fire provided.

I sneaked up on the boys from the dark and startled them a little by demanding:

"What is this, a hobo camp?" It pleased me to be able to arrive triumphantly and present the hard-won treasures from the store. I told them the story of the brush with the police, and got a sense they'd been getting concerned about my whereabouts.

"Thought maybe you'd run off with all the money," Tackett joked.

Suddenly all was right with the world. Our bellies were full on good food as we spread out our bedrolls by the warm fire. The starry night had us gazing into the great distance above, and in time we started musing about the folks back home.

"I wonder what Gay's up to right now?" Benjamin sighed.

"Gay?" Tackett repeated, then joked: "I'd have thought you'd be wondering what Alice Murphy was up to."

Benjamin ignored the remark and Duane changed the subject.

"I can just see our mom and sister," he mused. "They're probably sitting around listening to the radio tonight."

Mention of the radio prompted a spontaneous discussion of some of our favorite programs and songs. In no time the conversation led to a mention of the Mills Brothers, and had it not been for the need to remain undiscovered near the river we might've sung a medley of every Mills Brothers number we knew. We sat up until the fire embers were a deep red, then slowly nodded off to sleep. We knew we were close enough to the rail yards so that a train would announce its arrival to us. But with another eventful day finally spent, I don't think any of us would've cared if we'd simply slept through a couple of departures.

But it wasn't to be. As if predestined, as though we'd had guaranteed reservations, the clanging of an eastbound freight awakened us at around dawn. We were all still tired, but we'd only covered 300 miles in two days, and we knew the opportunity was too great to pass up. So we hurriedly got our grip together with the assumption the train had to be departing soon. Such was not the case. It just sort of stayed and idled in the yard for what seemed the longest time, and we didn't dare approach it for fear of what the cops had said.

There was nothing to do, then, but have a couple of sandwiches and wait to make our move.

"You don't suppose we'll finally be getting out of Washington for good," Tackett said, stretching and yawning.

"Just getting out of Newport will do fine by me," I said. "I don't care if I never see this place again."

"Let's see," Duane calculated. "If we got out of Washington this morning, then maybe we'd make Montana later today. That'd only leave of us . . . ."

One more state: North Dakota. All of us could begin to appreciate just how far we'd come. We could start to see an end to the adventure. Moreover, we seemed to sense that the whole trip was somehow meant to be. Otherwise, why would the car have been impounded? Why would we miss the Blewett Pass cutoff at Peshastin? And why, just when we were at our lowest point of the adventure, would we be befriended by the benevolent Farmer Murphy?

No, it had to be meant. And at that moment, as the train started to look as though it had made final preparations to depart from Newport, I sensed that nothing bad would happen the rest of the way. By now we knew how to get on and off of trains, and we certainly knew better than to go up where we could be detected. The food was holding out just fine. And our spirits had made a drastic improvement over the day before.

What remained now was to be selective in picking our railroad car. We'd twice gone the ladder route, and that wasn't preferrable to any of us. The open boxcar out of Wenatchee had been a relatively princely way to travel, but we knew we'd be hard-pressed to be so fortunate as to find another empty car.

What we hadn't yet tried was a flatcar, mainly because none had availed itself. That was about to change. With little notice the train started to pick up significant speed, and we made a dash for the first flatcar. The plan provided for Duane and Benjamin to grab and climb aboard at the front of the flatcar, while Tackett and I boarded from the rear.

"Make sense, everybody?" I shouted.

"Yeah," Benjamin yelled, "but it's getting going pretty fast now."

We steadied our bundles, jogging along the tracks with the train, waiting for the first flatcar to come along. Between cars I could see the courthouse up the hill, and I dreaded the thought that either police officer would be down here looking for us. Even if we got on and they saw us they were just the sorts to wire ahead to another jurisdiction and have us taken in again. No, we couldn't dare being seen again.

The flatcar suddenly was upon us, and it seemed to be flying by now faster than we could keep up. It would take precision coordination just to get our bundles aboard, let alone ourselves.

"Let's go," I yelled. "We can't wait any longer."

Up ahead Duane and Benjamin grabbed the short ladder in front of the flatcar and made a fairly deft boarding. That left just me and Tackett. I let him go first, but just as he'd tossed his grip aboard and grabbed the ladder something flew off the train.

"My smokes!" he shouted. "They've flown out of my pocket."

"Well," I yelled, barely clinging to the ladder, "there's nothing we can do about it now. We can't go back for them."

Tackett threw himself onto the flatcar and rolled into the middle of the platform. I swung aboard, but suddenly noticed another object fly by. Now my own pack of Luckies was tumbling back through the gravel along the tracks.

"Oh, no," I groaned, and I rolled over into the middle of the flatcar and looked up at the others.

I scrambled to my feet and patted my shirt pocket.

''Tackett lost his cigarettes,'' I sighed, ''and so did I. ''Oh, well. At least we've still got two packs left.''

Then Duane patted his own shirt pocket. ''Uh, make that one pack,'' he said. ''I lost mine, too.''

The only one of us who'd had the sense to secure his smokes in his pants pocket was Benjamin.

Ah, well, we seemed to say, shrugging. At least we were moving. And at least we were finally out of Newport, Washington -- and this time for good.

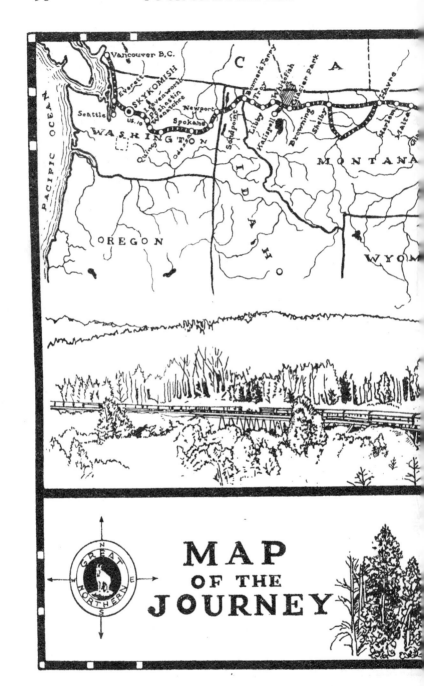

MAP OF THE JOURNEY

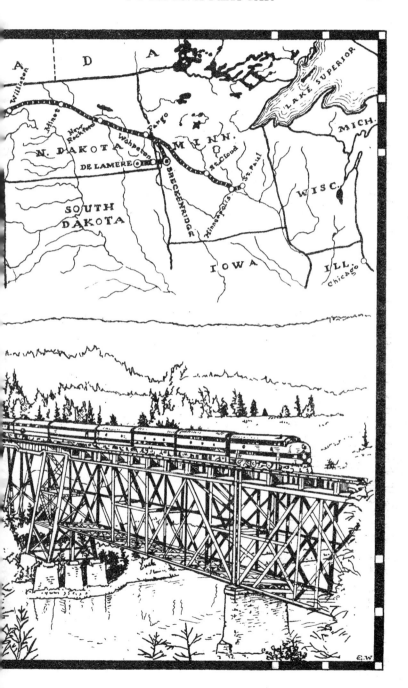

Chapter II

The rail-riding was familiar for us, but the mode was not. This time we'd finally caught a flatcar, and the experience was only marginally like that of boxcar riding. In a boxcar you were enclosed, and even though you had the sense of greater safety it was still possible to go flying off the train if you got too close to the open doors. A flatcar was something like the sensation kids of another generation would derive from skateboarding. Here you were: Standing on a flat platform that was making its way across the countryside. But the platform always seemed to be moving beneath your feet, and only a fool would venture anywhere near the edge of the deck. With no walls to grab hold of and your body swaying back and forth, you were best off staying in the middle of the platform.

But oh, was it ever fun. We sat for a while as we snaked alongside the Pend Oreille River up past Priest River again. We looked across from our place on the railroad tracks and strained to see the Murphy's spread through the trees.

"We're flyin' now, guys," Duane shouted, and we laughed and marveled about how far we'd come.

"Two states down, two to go," Tackett said.

"Yeah," Benjamin added, "but Idaho practically doesn't

count. The Panhandle's so skinny you can just about spit across it.''

''Like Rhode Island,'' Duane said, and I got to thinking about all the states there were that we'd heard about but never seen. I suddenly grew a little wistful as the wind blew through our hair where we sat on the flatcar platform.

''You know,'' I mused, ''I wonder what it would be like to just stay on these old trains, keep making connections and ride forever. We could see the whole country in time. Wouldn't that be terrific!''

''I wouldn't mind seein' Florida,'' Benjamin said. ''I'd like to see 'em wrestle those alligators down there.''

''Yeah,'' Tackett said, ''and Texas, of course -- see some real cowboys there.''

''You've sure got the right shoes for it,'' Benjamin kidded, tapping Tackett's bundle of grip that was made lumpy from the new cowboy boots he'd brought along.

''I imagine,'' I offered, ''that we'll see a few real cowboys come Montana,'' and just saying so made me appreciate the fact that we were really going to be there soon.

''Or New York City,'' Duane said.

''The Empire State Building, Yankee Stadium.''

''Madison Square Garden,'' Benjamin added, and took a few imaginary sparring shots with his fists.

For now the scenery was a good deal more rustic than anything in New York. The train coursed into Sandpoint and we thought briefly about maybe getting off and looking up Benjamin's relatives. The idea was abandoned, I think, because of the realization that the momentum was carrying us to our long-range destination. For now the ride was good and the pace was steady, and there was no reason to change plans. We weren't wanting for anything, as we all noted, digging in for more of Alice Murphy's sandwiches.

That inspired a little good-natured kidding from Tackett, who said: "Yeah, but the only problem, if we stayed on the train forever, is that Benjamin might never get to see Gay again. She'd probably be married and moved away by the time we ever got back to Seattle."

Then he winked at Duane and me, and added: "But then there'd always be pretty old Alice Murphy, eh Ron?"

Benjamin gave Tackett a gentle shove on the shoulder and played along.

"Yeah," he said, taking a bite from his sandwich, "if I ever do see your sister again I'll have to tell her I've met a girl who sure knows her way around the kitchen."

"Gee," Tackett said, "I'll have to remember to tell Gay you said so."

"At least," Duane intervened, "we'll always know where to get a great meal if we're ever in the vicinity of Newport."

"That," I said, "is the one place I never hope to go back and visit."

The train pulled out of Sandpoint past the landmark grain silo. In those days Sandpoint wasn't yet such a resort destination, serving more as a commercial hub for the Panhandle. In the summer the area around the silo could stink with rotting grain, and we were just as happy to ride up wind from the place and on toward Bonners Ferry. We were making really good time now, and could envision being in Montana by midday.

Bonners Ferry sat at the edge of the Kootenai Indian Reservation, but it wasn't much of a town in 1948. Mostly it was a road stop between Sandpoint and Canada, and we could find no reason whatsoever to get off there -- with the possible exception of our tobacco supply running low.

"Can you beat that," I said. "Four guys, and three of us lose our smokes."

"We'll definitely have to buy more at the next major stop," Benjamin said. "Duane and I will maybe dash into town and pick some up."

That seemed to be a good plan. For now it sufficed to note that we'd made what seemed to be our northernmost venture so far, as the tracks out of Bonners Ferry quickly skirted back toward the south and east, and drew a bead on the wide state of Montana.

There was no marker for entering the Big Sky country. In fact, slipping through the forests there was nothing to indicate you'd left Idaho and entered Montana. The only indication came when we abruptly pulled into Troy.

"Gee," Tackett said, "why stop in this tiny place?"

He had a good point, too. Troy, Montana, was but a burg of about 500 souls in those days. Just south of the railroad tracks was a semblance of a downtown area, with a row of wood-frame shops and a schoolyard another block down. Highway 2 was farther south yet, though most of the road traffic wound up looping through Troy proper for gas and supplies. The town actually was seeing its best days back then, because the forest industry was doing better than it would in the latter decades of the century.

The other important function of Troy, we later learned, was that of crew-changing station for the railroad. Crews worked sort of like relay-race teams. A crew would hop onto an east-bound freight out of Spokane and ride as far as Troy. Then that crew would get off and another would come aboard. The original crew would wait for a west-bound train and take it back to Spokane. The extra cabooses that sat idle on the rows of side tracks toward town were for crew members to sleep in if they needed to do so between runs.

These crews provided Troy with a source of retail trade, which was fortunate for us. Our main care was whether there would be a store to sell us smokes, and it just so happened there was one within an easy dash of where our freight finally lugged to a stop.

"This is our chance, I guess," I said. "Tackett and I will stay back and look after the stuff while you fellas make a run for it. Just don't dawdle, okay? Because we don't know how long we'll be here."

I knew I sounded a little like a parent when I lectured the guys. Then again, somebody had to be responsible for what we were doing. Lord knows, I wanted to have fun on this adventure as much -- maybe more -- than the other guys. But at 17 I was starting to feel a greater sense of responsibility than I had as a younger kid. I knew, after all, that a lot of boys my age or not much older already were getting married, having kids and settling down with jobs. That would've been the last thing on my wish list that summer, but I still was feeling more mature.

And maybe that's why it suddenly dawned on me after Benjamin and Duane got too far away for me to yell to them.

"Geez, Tackett," I said. "Do you realize we don't even have a plan laid out for if we get separated?"

Tackett, of course, was the kid of the group. As far as he was concerned, nothing was going to go wrong. If anything happened, the older guys would figure out how to deal with it. Hadn't I been the one to approach the farmer's house when we were all starving the night before? I'd always figure out something.

"Ah, don't worry, Jerry," Tackett said. "We're not gonna get separated."

Sometimes I wonder whether the act of just saying something makes it more likely to happen. Maybe that's why so many people are superstitious: knocking on wood to break some imagined jinx after they've spoken something that they fear might happen. Maybe I should've knocked on wood. Then again, it was too late now, because slowly, barely perceptibly, the train was starting to move.

"Uh," Tackett said cautiously, "is it just me, or was that a tug?"

"Maybe they're just positioning the train to take on a car," I said, nervously. "I mean, we've only been stopped here a few minutes."

A few minutes, of course, was about all that was required for a crew change. Then again, we didn't have any idea at the time that Troy served such a function.

I checked my wristwatch, then realized the futility of doing so. What difference did it make how long Duane and Benjamin had been gone? What mattered was that we were leaving and they were nowhere to be seen.

In fact, we wouldn't have been able to see them anyway, I realized. In the time it took for Tackett and me to realize what was going on, the train had moved east a ways from where it had been when the others got off. Even if they sprinted back to where they'd departed, our flatcar would be well beyond that point.

And then the sinking feeling hit me: Something terrible is about to happen here. I'm about to become separated from my brother and my friend.

In an instant I perceived the consequences. If we got separated, there would be no way beyond happenstance to make connections again. Sure, Tackett and I could make the next town, Libby, and wait for the other two. But how would we find them if they were somewhere aboard a long freight train? And how would we even know when the next train was coming through? Would they wait in Troy for us to turn around and come back from Libby? Would we keep passing each other back and forth forever?

Moreover, what would happen to my younger brother? My mom had stressed that my one greatest responsibility on this trip was to look after Duane. And now here we were: Tackett and me aboard a flatcar that was picking up speed, and now we were so far out of sight of the town and train yard that I wasn't sure if I'd ever even see him again.

"Tackett," I shouted, "I think we've got to get off of this train."

"But they'll make it," Tackett said. "They're fast runners. They didn't have that far to go, did they?"

"Maybe they stopped to use the restroom somewhere. Maybe there was a long line at the store. Anything could have happened. All I know is that we're going and they're nowhere to be seen."

It was the closest I'd ever come to sheer panic. The bundles of belongings sat before us like orphans as I searched the tracks behind us to see if they were coming on the run. But there was no sign whatsoever, and the train was chugging so fast that I wondered whether we even could jump off without breaking a leg.

"I'm telling you we've got to jump, Ron," I commanded, and with that I scooped up a pile of belongings and saw to it Tackett did, too.

"I don't know about this," Tackett yelled, warily.

"It's our only option," I said. "Toss that stuff and jump, and try to land softly like you're a paratrooper."

"But I'm not one," Tackett protested.

"I mean like in the movies," I yelled, and with that I tossed the belongings away from the train and followed them through the air.

Landing from a moving platform, I found, is a lot trickier

than jumping from a stationary object. Even though I'd tried to coach Tackett in the art of hopping off a train, I found myself wanting a little. I hit with a double thud on the balls of my feet, then went head over heals, catching sight of Tackett doing the same a ways up the tracks. We were both off, with the belongings scattered around us. We were scuffed up a little from the gravel in the rail bed, but otherwise everything was right with the world.

Or it would've been had we not looked up in time to see a couple of familiar faces. Duane and Benjamin were clinging to boxcar ladders as the train seemed to speed past. They'd made it, all right. But we'd gotten off.

"Tackett," I yelled, "hurry and grab the stuff again. They're aboard. C'mon, let's try to get back on!"

We fumbled with the belongings, and I sensed there was no way we'd be able to get aboard such a rapid freight. Somehow, though, I knew we had to try. I arbitrarily grabbed two bundles and brought them back for the heave-ho. But Tackett had another idea, and just as I let go of the bundle and it plopped onto an empty flatcar I heard him scream:

"Jerry! No! Don't!"

I turned just in time to see what I'd done. I'd thrown the belongings onto the train at about the instant Duane and Benjamin had bailed out. More specifically, I'd thrown away one of Benjamin's sleeping bags and the bundle with Tackett's fresh clothes, and those fancy cowboy boots we'd been hauling around with us.

"Jerry!" Tackett was enraged. "How could you do that? Throw away all my stuff like that? What's the matter with you, you goofball?"

I felt terrible about it, but I also felt helpless. By now the train had left us standing in the summer dust. I was incredibly relieved that we hadn't gotten split up, but I knew what

Tackett was feeling, too. And there just wasn't much I could say that would change anything.

"Hey," Benjamin shouted at Tackett, "quit your bitching If anybody's got a right to have a beef, it's me. I didn't just lose a sleeping bag. I lost a whole car on this trip."

We all stared at the ground for a minute or so. Then Duane broke the ice.

"Hey," he said, his enthusiasm never waning, "what are we getting so steamed about? We've still got each other, don't we? We've still got the trip."

Benjamin added, gamely: "Yeah, and hey! We got the smokes."

But Tackett wasn't ready to forgive and forget quite yet, and I sure couldn't blame him.

Chapter 12

An optimist might be able to cite two advantages that sprung from when I threw our bundle onto the flatcar, which hauled it off to some point east. One: Some hobo no doubt thought it was Christmas in July when he discovered the treasure somewhere down the line. We'd likely never know about that.

The other bright spot -- if you wanted to look at it that way -- was that the four of us suddenly didn't have nearly as much stuff to lug around, but I didn't dare bring it up. I could tell, as we assessed our situation, that it would take some doing to get back into Tackett's good graces.

Our situation was that we were a little roughed up from the on-again-off-again boarding fiasco. Duane had a scraped arm and was bleeding a little, but a 15-year-old kid doesn't think much about such an injury. Nobody had any broken bones: That was the main thing. Both Rons had lost some clothes, and of course one of us would be faced from here on out with nights on which we had no bedding. Now there was just one sleeping bag between us, plus the blankets my brother and I had brought from home.

It was getting toward late afternoon by then, so we decided we'd go explore in Troy. The town was extremely picturesque in those days, nestled in a valley of the sprawling, rugged Kootenai National Forest. The Kootenai River flowed by between the town and the highway. The town sustained itself on revenue from the nearby lumber and plywood mills, and of course the railroad had made its economic impact. Years earlier, during the 1890s, settlers had rushed into Troy on the promise of staking silver and copper claims, and years later the slow death of the timber industry would take a heavy toll on the people of Troy.

But at mid-century it was a thriving burg, and we noted signs of prosperity as we headed through town. For the life of us we couldn't figure out why such a relatively small place would be a regular -- albeit brief -- railroad stop, but that question was answered at a filling station, where we stopped for a map. The attendant told us about the crew changings, and we figured out the rest for ourselves.

The attendant didn't seem to mind if we hung around for a while, so we spread out the map and admired our progress. It's difficult to believe from a modern perspective, but road maps were free in those days. You could have all you wanted. And when you took a car in for gas, the attendants normally checked your tires and looked under the hoods. Cars were such then that just about anybody who ran a station knew how to work on them, and folks tended to hang around a friendly gas station back then.

"This is our third state already," Tackett boasted to the attendant. "Only one more to go before we get to where we're going, so we're more than halfway there."

The attendant was amused by the assertion.

"I'll agree with you, son," he said to Tackett, "that you're on your third state. But you're nowhere near halfway to Breckenridge. Nah, you're only 400 miles out of Seattle right now. Minnesota's nearly three times that far away.

Why, Montana's over 700 miles across all by itself. North Dakota's close to 400.''

This was a sobering fact for all of us to consider. It seemed as though we'd come so far, but then when you looked at the map it was pretty clear what we were faced with.

''See,'' the attendant continued, gesturing with a sweep of his hand to the breadth of Montana, ''you've got just about the widest place in the country for traveling and still being in the same state. Folks drive all day here and don't even make it half way across the Big Sky country. No, you've still got a lot of trip ahead of you.''

Then, as we looked at one another in amazement and considered the geographical obstacle we faced, the attendant added one more morsel to chew.

''The other thing is,'' he said, ''is once you get through Montana, you still got to get all the way across North Dakota -- and it's half as wide as Montana.''

With that I slowly folded the map and we shuffled off toward the outskirts of town again.

''Nice of that guy to cheer us up,'' Tackett deadpanned.

''Looks to me,'' Benjamin sighed, ''as if we're kind of in the middle of nowhere.''

But I didn't see it that way, and I know Duane didn't, either. As long as the four of us had each other's company, how could you say we were ''nowhere?'' The way I saw it, the center of the world was where ever we happened to be at the moment, and if we were in Troy, Montana, then what of it? We wouldn't be staying here forever . . . would we?

''You know,'' Benjamin said as we settled in the shade near the railroad yard, ''when we first talked about extending this trip to back to where your dad lives, I guess it never occurred to me just how far DeLamere really is.''

"Three times as far as Seattle," Tackett said, repeating what the attendant had told us.

I began to sense a crisis of confidence coming. Suddenly I wondered whether the boys were having second thoughts about the adventure. Should I put it to a vote? All in favor of turning tail and catching a westbound to Seattle, say "aye." What if one said "yes" and the others disagreed? What if three were in favor and I was the only one holding out for DeLamere? I thought about how to phrase the question. Then something happened that made me realize maybe I wouldn't have to after all.

The little kid couldn't have been much older than 9. He had on an old red-flannel ball cap and wore denim overalls, with sandals and no socks. His face was slightly dirty from a smear of candy, and he approached us cautiously on a beat-up two-wheeler that was a size too big for him. He looked us over, one by one, keeping his distance in case we proved hostile in some way. We stared back at him, none of us saying a word.

Finally he said in a gruff little voice: "You fellas ain't from around here, are ya."

"Not likely," Duane said.

"You'd have probably seen us before if we were," Tackett added.

"What's your name, squirt?" Benjamin demanded.

"Jimmy," he said. "I live over past that schoolyard."

"Well, Jimmy," I said, trying to sound friendly, "the truth is that we come from way out by the Pacific Ocean, way over in Seattle, Washington."

Jimmy thought about that a second. "That's a long way away for sure," he said.

"Yeah," Duane said, "it's about 400 miles."

"Well," Jimmy said, "you ain't hoboes, are ya?"

We had another chuckle.

"Not yet, we aren't," I said, "but we're sure riding the rails like hoboes."

"We're headed half way across this wide country," Benjamin smiled.

"And we've seen plenty so far," Tackett added.

"Like what?" Jimmy wanted to know.

"Well," I smiled, "somebody tell Jimmy about the . . . about the Tunnel of Doom!"

Jimmy's eyes began to widen, as Tackett launched into a very well embellished version of the ride through the Cascade Tunnel. In Tackett's version we'd each nearly been jolted off the train a few times, then been attacked by rabid bats and nearly electrocuted by the engine.

Then Benjamin took over and told about how we landed in jail in Newport. This time, though, the jailers had been like ruthless prison guards, shackling us to the walls and beating us mercilessly.

"The only way we could escape," Benjamin assured Jimmy, whose mouth now gaped open in amazement, "was to whistle in Morse code through the dungeon bars so that a pretty lady in a bakery down the street would hear and bring us a cake with a file in it. Took us days just to file through the chains."

"Wow!" Jimmy finally exclaimed. "But how'd you get a hand free if you were shackled up?"

I could see we were on the verge of straining credulity beyond what the kid would believe, so I said:

"Let's just say it wasn't easy."

"But the hard part," Tackett said, "was dodging all those bullets from the railroad detective as we came into Troy a while ago. You must've heard all that gun fire, I'll bet."

Jimmy nodded to indicate maybe he had. We were having

a great time with him, and telling the increasingly tall tales was giving us a new sense of pride in what we'd accomplished. Okay, so maybe we hadn't really been shot at. But we had been to jail, by golly, and we had been hassled by the police. And that tunnel ride . . . well, there sure could've been bats in there.

When we were through with our yarns, Jimmy finally spoke.

"Well," he said, "sounds to me like you fellas are desperate characters, all right. You'll have no problems down at the hobo camp, I guess."

We surveyed one another's expressions, and I spoke first. "How's that again, Jimmy?"

"Well," he said, "you're new here and all, so you probably haven't heard. Down the Kootenai a ways, just out of town, there's a big ol' hobo jungle where the tramps from the trains come and go. It won't mean nothin' to you fellas, though, I expect, all the stabbings and gun play and everything."

Tackett spoke next.

"Come again, kid?" he said, tentatively. "Yeah," Jimmy said, his voice growing almost grave, "the whole town knows about it. But the county sheriff's even afraid to go down there at night -- even after one of them bums comes up to town and steals a kid from its bed."

Now we sensed maybe it was the kid who was telling the tall tales.

"Gee, Jimmy," Duane laughed, "you don't really believe that, do you?"

Jimmy didn't change his expression at all. "I wouldn't maybe if I hadn't seen the bodies floatin' in the Koot,"

Benjamin laughed nervously and said: "Bodies? What bodies?"

"Lot's of 'em," Jimmy insisted. "Those hoboes, they kill kids and murder each other, then throw the bodies into the river. I seen 'em."

Duane rolled his eyes.

"Anyway," Jimmy said, "you guys won't be scared, I'll bet."

He pointed off west through the trees toward the river.

"Just follow on down the bank," he assured us. "You'll find it."

And with that he turned his bike around and scrambled off toward home.

"Hey, Jerry," Benjamin asked, "do you believe any of that stuff could really be true?"

All of a sudden I realized they were all three looking at me expectantly.

"Ah, c'mon, you guys," I scoffed. "You certainly didn't believe any of that mumbo-jumbo, did you? That stuff's right out of 'Tom Sawyer' and 'Huck Finn.' That kid just turned the tables on you for that jazz you were giving him. He just got even with you."

"Well, of course we didn't believe it," Duane said, "but you never know about some of these things."

"I'll tell you what, guys," I smiled. "About midnight we'll seek out the local cemetery and see how many grave-robbers we can spot. Ha, ha, ha!"

"Duane," Tackett said, "your brother thinks he's real funny."

"Okay, guys," I said, apologetically, "I was only teasing. Let's go down to the river and check it out."

Tucked below the trees growing on the steep slopes of the Kootenai range, Troy was liable to grow dark early even during the dead of summer. By now, as we gathered up what was left of our grip and headed toward the river, it was late afternoon and already looking like dusk. No trains had come through in either direction, and we decided it was probably best to make camp and spend the night.

We followed the river a ways as it headed slightly northwest out of Troy. Tackett broke the silence suddenly, turning with a start and saying: ''Whoa! Was that a dead hobo floating in the river?''

We all laughed. And I think we all secretly wondered when we would come upon the alleged hobo camp. Finally we came around a river bend and saw a small clearing that looked as though it had been occupied before.

''Here's your hobo camp,'' I said. ''Only no hoboes, I guess.''

''Except us,'' Duane laughed, and we threw down our belongings.

''I don't know about you guys,'' I said, ''but I could sure go for a nice, cool dip right now.''

Within seconds we'd stripped down and started diving into a calm pool. We spent the better part of the rest of the afternoon frolicking in the water, and by early evening we'd worked up a pretty fair appetite again. There were still a few of Alice Murphy's famous sandwiches left, but Duane proposed something different.

''Why don't we,'' he said, ''break off some pieces of bread and see if we can lure some trout out of the water?''

I guess we all knew that we couldn't catch any fish this way. But we could sure dream. And as those fish darted up out of the pool to pick at the miniscule bits of bread we tossed in, I dreamed of a nice, hot dinner of pan-fried trout.

It remained a dream. In time we tired of the ''fishing'' expedition and gathered the wood for the evening campfire. Tonight there'd be no need to make ourselves inconspicuous, the way we'd been in Newport. We were far enough from town so that no one would detect us, and so far nobody has ordered us out of town.

At the same time, there was the lingering recollection of what Jimmy had told us. This was, after all, a hobo camp -- whether it was occupied by real hoboes or not. There was always that chance that someone would stumble in from the night and make things bad for us.

On the other hand, we were strong kids and there were four of us. If necessary, we knew we could fight every bit as fiercely as a grown man. And I doubted whether any hoboes would travel in packs of four or more. Surely we'd have them outnumbered if it came to a fight.

For now, though, we had the warm fire, the sandwiches and the memories of the tales we'd spun for Jimmy. We laughed and joked, told stories and talked about the fun we were having, and I knew then that at least one crisis of confidence had faded away. Besides, this trip hadn't been born out of need or desperation. It was a journey born of adventure, of excitement, of the need to find something different. We knew we could survive now. We were survivors who had been put to the test many times in just a few days. We'd come this far and were darned proud of it.

Still, as the embers flickered and we finally quieted down for the night, I couldn't help but wonder if the others weren't thinking what I was thinking: What if there really had been some hobo violence down this way? What if the county sheriff really was afraid to come down here? What if some of Jimmy's hobo stories had basis in the truth? Nah, couldn't be, could it?

As I lay back on my bedroll my last conscious thoughts were of the sky. The moon was out and shining brightly. The stars seemed so close you could almost touch them. Yet the sky was cluttered with tiny white balls of clouds. The reflection of the moon off the clouds gave them an iridescent glow, and I thought to myself: Those aren't clouds, they're little puffs of moonlight.

Chapter 13

J've always been one of those persons who dreams a lot. In fact, sleep and sleeping disorders would nearly prove to be the death of me years later. On this night, camped along the Kootenai under the stars above Montana, I dreamed with more depth and vividness than I had for a long time. This was in contrast to my usual manner of dreaming, when I'd wake up unaware of a lot of the details. Then, as was usually the case, I'd lapse back into slumber, determined to get back to the dream I'd left behind. But I wasn't able to do it. The dream would've escaped.

One of the vivid recurring dreams I experienced that night had its beginnings from when I was a young boy on our farm in DeLamere. It must've been about 1937 or '38. I dreamed that for some reason I was supposed to get up and go milk the cows. The problem was that there was a giant polar bear sitting in the farm yard, halfway between the house and barn. He refused to let me pass. To this day I wonder: Why a polar bear in a farm yard? Did I see a picture in a book? Did the bear represent some other obstacle or fear?

Then I got into the teen years, where we begin to learn that there definitely are differences between boys and girls. Even though I was shy around girls, it didn't keep me from dreaming about them. One night I fell asleep and imagined that four gorgeous hunks of feminity were chasing me -- me! Jerry Jacobson! They were laughing and giggling -- having great sport with me. Why I was trying to get away from them is anybody's guess. Probably it was due to the shyness that I was only too aware of. Anyway, they finally cornered me. Still laughing and giggling, they grabbed me and rassled me to the ground.

Yeah, but just then I woke up and realized I needed to go to the bathroom. All the way to the bathroom and back I pleaded: "Please, Lord, let me go back to that dream." Not a chance. I dreamed again, all right, and it was a dream about being cornered. But this time it was about a giant skunk cornering me at a golf driving range. The range was surrounded by netting 75 feet high, and I had to climb all the way to the top to escape. It was one of the few times I was glad to hear the alarm clock go off.

But on this night near Troy, Montana, I dreamed of those fish nearby in the Kootenai River, a few feet from where we slept. It may have been the gurgling of the water so close to us that inspired the dream. Maybe it was from sleeping out in the fresh air. Or it could've been from the sight of the trout flitting to the right and left after our little tidbits of bread. But in my dream I held a rod and reel. On my very first cast into the very same hole where we'd been swimming, I hooked what felt like a big one.

"You got him, Jerry," Benjamin said. "Play him good, now. Don't let him get away. He's gotta be at least four pounds."

I played him for all I was worth. Reeling him in near shore, he started to tire and I called for Duane to grab me a net. Duane dashed for the net, while the two Rons screamed their encouragement.

"Duane," I yelled, "Duane, hurry it up!"

And then I sat bolt upright. It was pitch black except for the stars and a few coals that still glowed from the fire. The others remained asleep, and I sat there for a moment, knowing that there wasn't any fish or rod or net. There was only a dream leftover, and I somehow knew that going back to sleep wouldn't restore it for me. Instead it brought back another faint recurring image. This was of Duane and me playing golf at Jackson Park in Seattle. We see Dad up ahead in the distance, but every time we hit an approach shot and think we'll catch up to him he recedes in the distance. Finally, on this night at the hobo jungle, we actually catch up with the man. But when he turns and looks at us, we see that it isn't Dad at all. It's a hobo with a menacing look in is eyes.

By morning I was nearly exhausted just from the dreams. Again I was the first to awaken, and I sat and surveyed the territory, then looked over the map until the chirping and squawking of the birds prompted the others to open their eyes.

"What day is it?" Tackett asked, rubbing his eyes.

"Judging from the map," I said, "it looks like today might just be the day we conquer the Rocky Mountains."

But there were a few matters to settle first. For one, we'd finally eaten the last of the sandwiches. There was a little money left, but not much. We decided one good way to economize would be to skip packaged cigarettes and just buy papers and a bag of Bull Durham.

"I guess," Duane laughed, "we're real hoboes now if we're rolling our own smokes."

We dropped into a grocery store in Troy and got some bare-bones food supplies for the next leg of the trip. About all we could afford was bread, cold cuts and some cheap margarine to moisten the sandwiches.

"These'll never taste like the ones Alice made, right Ron?" Tackett kidded.

The next item on the agenda had to do with transportation. We figured an eastbound freight would wander through sometime in the morning, so we hung around the yard waiting and looking over our situation.

"Under the best of circumstances," I said, "we'd make Breckenridge in three days. But that would be if we made every train connection and nothing unexpected happened between now and then."

Duane thought it was pretty funny when I said "unexpected."

"Don't know if you've noticed, Jerry," he said, "but everything we've done since we left Seattle has pretty much been unexpected."

"Okay," I conceded, "then let's just say extraordinarily unexpected."

"Like if we get stabbed and thrown into the Koot by murderous hoboes," Tackett joked.

"Nah," Benjamin added, "because we'd shoot 'em first."

I had to hand it to them: They were pretty lively for guys who were down to their last few cents and provisions. The last thing I wanted was to put a damper on anybody's enthusiasm, but I felt duty bound to at least talk about where we were and where we were going.

"I figure," I said, "that we'll be getting pretty hungry about two days from now -- that's unless we find a pot of gold or something. So that means we'd probably better figure on not lollygagging in any one place too long. Best to get back to DeLamere."

"All we need is a ride," Tackett said.

But one didn't come right away, so we passed the time

lagging pebbles at a piece of side track. It's amazing how competitive the smallest contest can get between boys, who don't mind spending hours at such pursuits. Fortunately it was less than an hour before the eastbound came, and knowing what we did about how brief a time it would linger in the yard, we knew we had to make our move.

"What'll it be, guys?" I asked. "Boxcar? Flat?"

"How 'bout something different this go-around, Jerry," Duane said, and just then we spied an empty gondola made to order for us.

"Step aboard, passengers," Tackett said, and within minutes we were moving again.

With every fresh train-hopping experience I was reminded anew just how exhilarating it could be. And each car had its singular charms. If the boxcar was like sitting in a moving living room with picture windows and the flatcar was like a skateboard, the gondola was more like commanding our own over-sized chariot. It was like something out of "Ben Hur," and it didn't take too vivid an imagination to look up ahead at the puffs of smoke and soot, and imagine the train engine as a great black steed pulling the chariot up toward the sky.

For that was our general direction. I figured we had about 200 miles to Marias Pass and the crest of the train route through the Rockies, and what a way to get there. My only worry was that the car would get stalled or sidelined or rerouted in one of the upcoming towns, but the guys clearly weren't in a worrying mood.

Oh, if you get to heaven
    (Oh, if you get to heaven)
Before I do,
    (Before I do),

Just bore a hole
    (Just bore a hole)
And pull me through.
    (And pull me through).
Oh, yes, if you get to heaven
Before I do,
Just bore a hole
And pull me through.
I ain't gonna grieve my Lord no more,
I ain't gonna grieve my Lord no more,
I ain't gonna grieve my Lord no more,
I ain't gonna grie-e-e-ve my Lord no more.

It seemed as though we sang that song all the way into Libby. In the back of my mind, though, I was still keeping track of the hours and days that lay before us. On a flat map it may not look very far from Troy through Libby and on through Whitefish and up toward Marias Pass. But I knew it was going to be quite a pull. The Rockies were a lot higher than the Cascades, and Marias -- an even mile high -- was a full 2,000 feet above Stevens Pass. Even if we could average 20 miles an hour (uphill and down) it would take us a good 10 hours just to get down toward Browning and Shelby, not counting stop-over time in any other towns such as Whitefish. And that still left us three-fifths of Montana to cross, not to mention North Dakota.

So we were in for a haul, no doubt about it. Libby came and went without incident. Then we snaked along Highway 2 for what seemed like hours before making Kalispell and Whitefish. But the ride was comfortable, especially when you figured gondolas were usually used to haul ore. I would've expected for there to be all kinds of dust and residue, but the car was clean enough so that you could sit down, sprawl out and make yourself at home. The railing was about five feet high -- just perfect for leaning your arms against the warm metal and gazing out at the mountain greenery and finally across the Flathead Valley.

It was late in the evening when we stopped at Kalispell, but we didn't have as prolonged a stop as we expected. We were aware that this particular Great Northern Railroad division was named for Kalispell, but the division point now was at Whitefish: 15 miles to the north. While Kalispell had been the main division point, one particular grade was quite steep. A better passage was eventually discovered up north, though Kalispell remained the commercial center of the Flathead Valley.

By the time we made Whitefish it was about as dark as the night would get, and that could cause a problem. In the dark it would be just about impossible to tell where our gondola was being routed, and since it was presumed to be empty we figured there was a good chance that it wouldn't be empty for long. We just hoped it wouldn't get side-tracked, sending us in search of yet another ride over the pass.

"My guess," I said to the others, "is that we'd be fools to leave this car if we don't have to."

"I'm with Jerry," Duane said, and the others agreed.

It was the closest we felt like what a stowaway must experience, because all around us we could hear activity -- though nobody bothered to look into our car and see where we were hiding. All kinds of banging and clanging was going on, with shouts from railroad workers. I sneaked a peek over at the fine old Whitefish train station, part of which was destined to be made into a railroad museum. But the lights were faint and I couldn't make out any activity inside the station.

Finally, after what seemed an eternity of a delay, we felt a firm nudge and with it the unmistakable forward momentum only a train can provide. I pulled myself up to the gondola rail and peered over the side. The magnificent Whitefish station was indeed fading from view toward the west. We'd evidently made out okay. All that remained now was to continue that slow, steady march up the terrain to mile-high Marias Pass.

After an hour or so we gave up on the vigil and decided we were too tired to wait up for that magic moment when the train inevitably would cross the Continental Divide. As I gradually was lulled to sleep I could appreciate just how slowly -- almost painfully -- the train was working its way to the summit. It reminded me of that kids' story about the Little Engine That Could: chugging along up the hill chanting ''I think I can, I think I can . . .''

The cadence was plenty to pacify me, and I slept that night a lot more dreamlessly than I had the night before. In the morning we awoke to a glorious sight: East Glacier National Park, just past Marias Pass. Abruptly the train picked up speed and began wending its way back down to the elevation of the Great Plains.

''Gee,'' Benjamin marveled, as the terrain changed as abruptly as the velocity, ''this reminds me just a little of when we came out of the tunnel.''

''Yeah,'' I pointed out, ''it's like going from one world to another in the snap of your fingers.''

True enough, we'd gone from sylvan beauty to brown, rolling hills.

''Pure grazing country,'' Tackett said. ''Look for cowboys.''

The remark reminded me that I still hadn't quite cleared the air with Tackett on the subject of his cowboy boots, and that nagged at me. I was hoping somehow I could do something to compensate for having lost the stuff, but for now it figured best for me to just bide my time and see what happened. The gondola was good for biding your time. It also was a good target for the morning sunshine, as my brother suddenly observed.

"Yeah," Duane said, rubbing his arms, "and there's another difference you guys may have noticed between this place and Wenatchee. Is it just me, or is it a lot warmer all of a sudden than it was yesterday at this time?"

Chapter 14

*E*ven though we'd set out in the dead of summer, the heat hadn't really been a factor during the adventure -- not until now, anyway. Teenage boys often seem capable of remaining indifferent toward extremes of cold and heat. Duane and I could play ball outside with no jackets in January or golf all day in the hot sun of August, and never once complain.

But there was a major factor that made it different as we rode along into the Great Plains in the gondola. The temperature that day would be typical of the high plains in July, meaning the low 100s wouldn't be out of the ordinary. But among our supplies we hadn't bothered to include any fluids, and even a kid in his mid-teens eventually has to concede that the combination of a hot day and no water eventually is going to take its toll.

Worse still: As comfortable as the gondola -- our chariot into the Rockies -- had been, the car could become a real pressure cooker in the heat. Since it was constructed of metal, it reflected heat and held onto it at the same time. The railings became hot to the touch, and the total effect was that of riding along in a hot frying pan. The brown, burned plains and hills also heightened the feeling of heat, and probably made us even more thirsty than we were.

The train, which we might've expected to pick up the pace now that it had cleared Marias Pass, made a deliberate stop in every small town. The first was Browning, which we found appropriate.

"Looking at the color of the hills and prairies around here," Tackett observed, "I can't think of a better name for this place than Browning."

Departing Browning we were at the western edge of the Blackfoot Indian Reservation. I imagined as we made our way up toward Cut Bank what it would've been like had I lived just a few generations earlier, when settlers learned the hard way that it didn't do to travel through this rough land where the fierce Blackfoot tribe roamed. By 1948, of course, all the reservation land was peaceful, and in time the area between Browning and Cut Bank would develop some fine Native American museums.

For now, though, the chance to see this desolate but historic land was something special for boys from the suburbs of Seattle, kids whose knowledge of such regions had been restricted to dry history books. Our knowledge of Indians was shaped by Western movies, which undoubtedly helped set our minds to wondering what it would've been like being attacked by Blackfoot warriors.

Mainly our appetites were under attack. At midmorning we made up some sandwiches from the dwindling supplies, but that didn't quite curb the thirst. We'd thought to bring along a couple of rolls of toilet paper, but we hadn't provided any beverages.

By the time we made Shelby we were unsure about whether it would be better to make a dash from the gondola and find some water, or whether the safer bet was to stay aboard. Experienced hoboes no doubt would've known to the second how long every train would linger at every stop.

Obviously we had no such advantage.

"Here's the way it is," Duane said as we idled in the yard at Shelby. "If we make a run for it, then the train will leave just as sure as I'm thirsty. But if we stay, then the train won't leave for another two hours."

So that was the problem. We couldn't afford to be left in Shelby, which was sort of a dead looking town even if it happened to be a major branch-line connection for trains going in all four directions. This was years before the completion of Interstate 15, which now leads directly down state to Great Falls. In those days the north and south railroad ran through Shelby and up into Alberta, and even though there weren't any great population centers to speak of in that region, the Shelby rail yard remained busy switching cars every which way.

We decided to sit it out. That meant a long wait and lots more anxiety about whether our car would get switched. After about half an hour Duane spoke again.

"See what I mean? If we'd gotten off when we got here we could've gone to town and taken the grand tour by now -- and we wouldn't be thirsty anymore."

"Well," I said, "we may still have enough time. I think we oughta risk it."

The train station wasn't more than 100 yards from our car. Dashing to the station and back might not take more than a couple of minutes, but another risk occurred to me. What if we were spotted coming and going from the gondola? But the thirst was biting at our throats and wrenching our stomachs, and we resolved to go.

"Should we split up again?" Benjamin wondered.

"Nah," Tackett reminded him, "we tried that, remember?"

It wouldn't do to leave the belongings unattended, so we

shouldered our grip and made a mad dash. Within seconds we were inside the train station, which, even though it wasn't well ventilated, remained cool compared with the heat of the gondola. The smell of the old rough-plank floors was a welcome relief from the hot metallic odor we'd been inhaling in the morning sun. We couldn't find a drinking fountain, but there was a restroom. Each of us took turns sticking our heads under the sink faucet and gulping up as much water as our bellies would hold.

''That tasted so good,'' Duane said, ''that I don't much care if we do miss the train.''

But I knew missing our ride would never do. We still had most of Montana ahead of us, and at this pace we'd starve before we got to DeLamere. We sprinted back to the gondola, which hadn't moved an inch. We all agreed the risk had been well worth taking, but it was still another half hour before the train rolled out. By then we were getting thirsty again.

With no protection from the heat, our only means of trying to stay cool was to rest our arms on the rail and lean out as far as possible, catching what little breeze might be available. I imagined what it was going to be like if we had to go another 800 miles like this, and suddenly wished we could do all our traveling at night when it was cooler. It wasn't possible, though, and just as I was wishing the train would at least speed up to create more air flow, just the opposite happened.

''Why are we stopping here?'' Benjamin wondered.

''Maybe it's an Indian ambush,'' Tackett grinned.

That seemed pretty farfetched, we realized, but there wasn't any ready explanation for chugging to a halt in the middle of nowhere. There was no town, no buildings of any kind -- nothing.

''Wait here,'' I volunteered, ''and I'll go up ahead and see what's going on.''

We knew there was nothing to the west of us or we'd have seen it when we passed. I crept up along side a few cars, being careful not to be detected. Soon I saw it: There was a side track in the middle of the prairie setting, with some corrals and loading ramps to run the cattle into stock cars. Evidently there were cattle ranches near by, where real cowboys were doing the everyday, less-than-glamorous business of tending livestock. It would've been interesting to go up farther ahead and watch them herd the cattle onto the cars, but I couldn't risk getting caught. If we got kicked off the train here, there was no telling what would happen to us. We could wander the prairie until we collapsed of thirst, as Tackett noted when I got back to the gondola and reported what I'd seen.

"I think I just saw buzzards circling around up there," he said, poking a limp finger toward the blistering sun.

"Yeah," Duane sighed, "when I think back to just two nights ago, when we were next to the Kootenai River. We could've had gallons of water to drink."

"That is," Benjamin added wryly, "if you don't mind drinking water with dead hoboes floating in it."

"Hey," I said, "let's stop talking about water for a while. You guys are just making me thirsty."

So there was nothing to do, really, but wait in the midday sun and see how long it would take to load up the cattle cars. This business of riding the rails could be the greatest joy or the most tedious annoyance. If there's anything a teenage boy likes less than waiting, it's waiting in the hot sun, with no shade and no water. After about 10 minutes of this I decided I wasn't going to wait anymore.

"I've got a hunch," I said, "that one of these boxcars must be hiding something from us -- something good."

The boys followed me down the tracks about 15 cars,

unsure of what I was up to. Finally I came to a boxcar that looked to be a likely candidate, and I said:

"Here goes nothing."

Benjamin said: "Jerry, what's the idea?"

"The idea is that we're hungry and I'm looking for food," I said, in a matter of fact manner.

"But breaking into a boxcar," Benjamin said. "Isn't it against the law?"

"That or starve." I said. I had to weigh the relative illegality of what I was doing against the prospect of our ongoing hunger. You make some awfully expedient decisions under such circumstances.

"You'll never be able to break that seal anyway," Tackett scoffed.

"Yeah? Just watch me," I said. The lock was a hasp-type arrangement with a metal marking strap and a slot. I worked the strap back and forth for a few minutes, It heated up in my fingers to the point where I had to hold it in my shirt tail. Finally it gave way, snapping like hot baling wire.

"Bingo," I said. "Now let's see what treasure lies beyond this door."

It took a couple of us to shoulder the boxcar door and shove it open far enough for the light to catch the containers.

"My lord, what have we here?" I said.

It was boxes upon boxes stacked orderly on pallets. Each box -- and there must've been hundreds of them -- held four one-gallon cans of cherries. I read from a box label:

"Product of Washington State. Boys," I marveled, "it looks as though it's a gift from the folks back home!"

The other three hooted and cheered.

"I could eat a case all by myself," Benjamin exclaimed.

But I realized that the cherries really were a gift of sorts. We probably could've broken into any 20 boxcars and only found pallets of feed bags or fertilizer or asphalt compound. Instead, we got just what we wanted on the first try. Now the trick was to be sure we didn't spoil our good fortune by getting greedy or careless -- or caught.

"Here," I said, hoisting a case each to both Rons. "You fellas each take one back to the gondola. These oughta hold us for a while. I'll stay and fix the seal as best I can."

I rigged up the seal so that it didn't appear tampered with, and made a mental note of the number on the boxcar. It could be, I figured, that we'd need to return sometime on the trip and shag more cans of cherries.

By the time I got back to the gondola the boys were each working open a cherry can with the opener blade of their jack knives. Tackett rocked and pried the blade until the juice came seeping out of the can

"Ah, nectar of the gods!" he declared as he licked it off the lid.

We each got a section of the lids opened and folded the lid back, slurping the juice and cherries, making joyful remarks about how wonderful it tasted.

"You know," Duane said, "this stuff is great, but right now I could really go for a quart of ice cream and pour this stuff over it and have a cherry sundae or a cherry float. Boy, that sounds good!"

"Holy cow," I yelled. I blurted it out so much louder and unexpectedly than I meant to that each of them instinctively jumped.

Benjamin was just lifting the can to his mouth and my sudden exclamation jolted him so that he slopped a bunch of it all over the front of his shirt.

"For crying out loud Jerry, now look what you did."

"I'm sorry Ben, "I said, "I didn't mean to startle you but I just remembered something."

''After scaring me out of a years growth and causing me to slop up my shirt, I hope you remembered something good.''

''Well, I think it's good. Do you remember when we were walking on top of those box cars just before we got to Newport?''

''Jerry,'' Duane responded, ''If you're asking us if we remember, being thrown in the 'pokey', of course we remember.''

''Thats not what I'm getting at. Do you remember that some of the boxcars we walked over had hatches on top?''

''Sure, but what has that got to do with anything?'' he wanted to know.

''Those were refridgerator cars.'' I answered.

So?'' Benjamin queried.

''So those hatch doors are where they load the big blocks of ice into the cars.''

''So, whats that got to do with us?'' Duane asked.

I looked them all square in the eye before answering.

''So, I can't offer you any ice cream, but I think I can offer you ice so you can have chilled cherries.''

All of a sudden their eyes lit up with the realization of what might be in store for us.

''How do you know there's ice in those compartments?'' Duane wanted to know.

''Quite some time ago I read in the newspaper that a hobo who was travelling through hot country got into one and--''

''He was probably going through Browning Montana,'' Tacket interupted.

''Well, anyway,'' I said, ''he climbed down into one of those ice compartments and accidently let the door close behind him. When he was finally discovered his body temperature was so low that he almost died.''

I now had their undivided attention.

"I noticed earlier that the second car in front of us is the same kind of refridgerator car that I saw before. I think that we can get some ice to chill the cherry juice at least. It's not as good as ice cream but at least its cold."

"I definitely think it's worth a try," Duane said.

The others agreed.

"Okay Duane," I said, "why don't you and Benjamin make a try for it: Don't let yourselves be seen. When you get to the top of the next boxcar crawl on your hands and knees. Whatever you do don't stand up and let yourselves be seen. And another thing," I said, "whatever you do don't both of you crawl into the compartment at the same time. We don't need any more hobo accidents. You understand?"

"Jerry and I will try to keep an eye out and warn you if anyone comes around." Tackett stated.

We watched them climb up the ladder to the top of the car in front of us and hoped that they wouldn't be spotted. I watched out one side of the gondola and Tackett watched out the other. There was little chance of detection since we were out in the middle of nowhere.

We really didn't have anything for them to carry ice in so they took a couple of extra shirts that they would wrap around the ice.

I knew that if they didn't come back shortly that I would go looking for them but I hoped that I didn't have to.

In just a few minutes they came crawling back over the boxcar in front of us. Two shirts full of chopped ice that they had chipped off with their knives.

We knew it wouldn't last long in this heat but for now we were satisfied. Cold cherries and juice. Ah, Delicious!

We opened the rest of the cans and ate some of the cherries and slurped the juice so we would have room for some ice in the cans. Otherwise the ice would just be wasted by melting away in this heat.

Later, after the train was moving again, we would make another trip to the refridgerator car but for now we were totally sated.

Finally Tackett looked over at me and, with approval in his eyes, said:

"I've got to hand it to you, Jerry. We needed something to eat and something to drink, and you were the guy who went out and got us both -- in the same can. And then you got us an ice box to chill it."

Benjamin and Duane seemed relieved by Tackett's remark. They both no doubt felt the strain that had developed after I accidentally lost the belongings in Troy. The last thing this adventure needed was hard feelings, and everybody knew it.

"Well," Benjamin said to Tackett, "then does this mean you're going to let up on Jerry for losing your cowboy boots?"

"Ah," Tackett grinned, "those new boots weren't very comfortable anyway. Besides, you can't eat or drink a pair of cowboy boots."

With that we all laughed and helped ourselves to some more of the fruit feast. I don't think cherries -- fresh or otherwise -- had ever tasted so wonderful as they did as we sat in that gondola. Seated behind the rail we couldn't be seen by anybody. We were in our own little world, gorged with food and waiting for the train ride to start up again.

Unfortunately, the start-up came none too soon. After another half hour, though, we felt the familiar lurching motion, and the gondola jerked ahead a few feet. Then it stopped and shot back a ways. Then it lunged forward again, then back, then forward.

"What in Hades is going on?" Tackett wondered out

loud.

It turned out that the engineer was using the play between couplings to work back and forth until he could pick up enough forward momentum to keep going. It was a common practice for very long trains on inclines. After a while we were heading east at our normal speed again. We were off in the direction of Havre, which cut another 150 miles from the endless breadth of Montana. At the pace we were moving we wouldn't make Havre until late evening. We were grateful by then for the relatively mild temperature that embraced us when the sun went down. There also was an advantage to being in the dark again, as each one of us noted then and for the rest of the night. That brings up another point about teenage boys: They can sit in a pasture and eat tree fruit all afternoon, or sit in a gondola and do the same. It never quite occurs to them until too late that even a big, strong kid needs a little variety in his diet.

As I say, we were just as glad we were in the dark that first night after our prolonged feast of canned cherries. But what we were even more grateful for was the fact that we'd had the good sense to pack in a couple of rolls of toilet paper.

Chapter 15

Those metal rails that had been so hot during the day were mercifully cool -- even cold at times -- when we used them at various times during the night. The humidity remained high at night, but the gondola wasn't a hot plate anymore, and for that we were all pretty thankful. The train had lingered for a while in Havre, which, like Shelby, was a major connection point for that part of the region.

The cherries indeed would bring a curse later after we pulled out of Havre, but they also solved the one problem that had nagged me since Troy. I now felt completely off the hook for having made the honest mistake of tossing away the belongings. It's not as though I'd purposely ditched the baggage, but I could see how Tackett had felt. If somebody had thrown away my new boots I probably would've been sore at them for a while too. And I was glad Tackett still felt happy about getting the unexpected cherry feast -- even under the moon at midnight, when one by one we'd take a seat on the rail and let nature take its course.

Given the condition of our innards, then, I can't say it was the most comfortable night's sleep of the adventure. But the train was moving along at a good pace, and I estimated that, with any luck and few delays, we could actually make

Williston -- the first significant town in North Dakota -- by the next night. That would at least put us in the same state as Dad. And it'd sure give us an emotional lift after the episodes we'd been through during recent days -- and nights.

The train really put some distance behind us during the night. It chugged through Harlem, Malta and Glasgow -- all these towns with names taken from other countries near and far. It was the middle of the night when we passed by the cluster of lakes just east of Malta. It would've made a really spectacular sight by day, I'm sure, but we were in for something just as scenic when, at dawn, we picked up the course of the Missouri River some 50 miles west of Wolf Point.

"Imagine that," Duane marveled. "The Missouri River. Now I really feel like we're getting somewhere."

And in fact we were. Out of Wolf Point it only would be a hundred miles or so to the North Dakota border.

"If we can get through Montana in this kind of weather," I proffered, "then, boys, I think we can get through about anything."

Tackett said: "Yeah, and it'll make it even easier to get through it if we can get some more tobacco."

Sure enough: We were about out of Bull Durham. Real commercially made cigarettes seemed to be a genuine luxury all of a sudden. Even a good half-smoked butt would be welcome, but smokes would cost money and we were out. Looking back on the adventure, we probably could've gotten as far as we had in royal fashion on no more than $20. That would've bought more and better food and enough cigarettes. As it was, we'd gone through half that much money and still managed to make out okay. Now, though, with Wolf Point approaching, it was clear we'd need to figure out how to get tobacco. And Duane and Tackett thought they had a plan.

"What we'll do," Duane volunteered, "is we'll just go to a store and see if we can sweep out the back room or something for a pack or two of smokes. All they can do is say 'no,' right?"

But I was thinking of what happened in Troy.

"I'm not sure," I said. "I just don't want to risk getting separated, not after we've come so far."

Benjamin suggested that all of us go.

"Nah," Tackett said, "it'd look like we were ganging up. It's better if just Duane and I go. We're younger and maybe they'll take pity on us."

I relented.

"But the plan is," I said, "that if the train starts to leave we all meet right here in the railroad yard. We don't want you guys coming back and hopping a moving freight train only to find out Benjamin and I are still back here in the yard."

They set out toward town and Benjamin and I scuffed around the train yard looking for cigarette butts. After a while we'd turned up several good sized ones, and we lit up and relaxed by the grip.

"Now I'm starting to feel like a real hobo," Benjamin said. "Something about smoking cigarette butts that will do that for you."

Then I looked around and realized we weren't alone. Standing at the other side of the gondola, looking us over, was a man who appeared to be in his 30s. He wore a tattered jackett and dirty pants, with old shoes and socks that slid down his ankles. His hair was pulled back and matted under a well-worn fedora with a grease spot on one side, and I knew immediately that what I was beholding was a genuine hobo.

"Howdy, boys," he said, gesturing vaguely with his hat and approaching us.

"Hi," I said, blankly. I wasn't sure how cautious to be,

though I was glad there were two of us and just one of him. I harked back to what little Jimmy had said in Troy a few days earlier. If nothing else, his fantastic claims had made me wary of strangers -- especially strangers who looked like this fellow.

"You boys ridin' the freight?" he asked.

I didn't want to reveal more than I had to.

"Right now we're just waiting for our two friends to get back from town, that's all," I said.

"How 'bout you, mister?" Benjamin asked. "You fixin' to hop on?"

The hobo chuckled a little.

"Well, son," he said, "I wouldn't know how to do much else after all these years. Yeah, I've been hoppin' freights since you boys were born, I expect. I could tell you some stories."

I decided there wasn't much harm in telling a little about our adventure. I gave him the bare bones version of what we'd done and where we were headed.

"Off to see your pop, eh?" he said. "That's real nice, boys. Yep, I've run into lots of boys in my time, ridin' the rails to get home to the folks. Not all of them really goin' home, I expect. Most of 'em runnin' away from home, like I did back in the early '30s."

The hobo didn't have any apparent belongings with him.

"You on this train?" I asked him.

"Maybe so," he said. "But if I am, I sure ain't ridin' in no coal car like you fellas. Too darned hot out here in summer."

"You're telling us," Benjamin said, wiping his brow.

"Let me give you boys a little advice," the hobo offered. "Watch out for thievin' if you're gonna be ridin' long. Some of these old boys out here on the trains, they aren't as nice a fella as I am. You'll think they are, but they'll steal you blind.''

I had to chuckle a little.

''Well, Mister,'' I said, ''not much chance of that. None of us four even owns much more than what's on our backs. I don't know what anybody would steal from us.''

He smiled and said: ''You'd be surprised, boys. Be real surprised. Just take my advice and don't get too friendly with strangers out here, especially if you plan on making it all the way to -- what was it now? -- DeLamere?''

He pulled what appeared to be a hand-rolled smoke out of his pocket, lit it and started back around the other side of the gondola.

''Wait a minute,'' I shouted toward him. ''You wouldn't happen to know what time this freight pulls out for Williston, would you?''

He laughed and said: ''Boys, I can tell you all about passenger trains, but the freights don't run on any set schedule. My guess is we won't be here longer than another 15 minutes. Let's just say you better hope your buddies get back on time, because there probably ain't another train comin' through here 'til after it gets awful hot in Wolf Point.''

''Now that was what I'd call a character,'' Benjamin said after the man had wandered off..

''Can you imagine,'' I said, ''that guy's spent the better part of two decades out on the rails like this.''

''Well,'' Benjamin said, ''the work's pretty easy, I guess. But he doesn't seem to have much to show for it, does he.''

''Except memories,'' I said, ''which is what we'll have, too.''

And we most assuredly would have that much. It was safe to say that when this was all over -- assuming nothing dire awaited us -- the scraped elbows and upset stomachs and bad bowels and lost belongings all would be de-emphasized. If not forgotten, surely they'd be put into their proper perspective. The wounds would heal, but the memories would continue and grow more vivid with every retelling. Slowly, I realized, this trip was contributing to the way the four of us would define ourselves, perhaps for as long as we lived.

Meeting up with the hobo served a couple of purposes. For one, it confirmed for me that we needed to be wary -- even though we were having the time of our life. It also reminded me of how good it was that we had places to go and people to see. We weren't just a bunch of hoboes out on the rails, wandering forever. There was DeLamere in the distance, and Dad was there. He had no way of knowing, of course, that we were coming, but I was sure he'd be glad to see us. Even if Dad hadn't taken to life in Seattle, I knew he must've harbored some emotions toward us boys. That's what I wanted to believe as we waited there for my brother andTackett, who suddenly seemed perilously close to missing the train.

"If that bum knew what he was talking about," Benjamin said, eyeing his watch, "then Duane and Ron had better beat it pretty soon or we're stuck here."

I checked my watch: no more than 10 minutes to departure, and no sign of them.

"Maybe I should dash in and look for them," I said. "But what good would it do? I'd never make it back by departure time anyway."

Then in the distance we could see them running. They were going top speed, and as they approached we could see that they looked more anxious than they should've if they were merely worried about catching the train.

"Hop on," Duane yelled, "and we'll tell you everything that happened."

Just then the train started moving, precisely as the hobo had said it would. We decided to give up on the hot gondola, instead selecting a flatcar that was partially occupied by farm equipment -- a hay baler and a corn harvester. Duane and Tackett each pulled a pack of Luckies from their front pants pockets and when they caught their breath Duane began to tell their tale.

"We found this old drug store," he explained. "Went in and told the guy we were ridin' the freight and out of money and all. We told him we were real desperate to get some smokes and willing to do whatever to earn a couple packs."

"He must've believed us," Tackett said, "because he seemed real understanding and asked us right away what kind of cigarettes we smoked."

"Yeah," Duane said, "because he went behind his counter, reached in and pulled out two packs of Luckies and tossed them to us."

"Then the funny part happened," Tackett said. "We were just standing there looking across the store at him, and he walked back to the back room and said: 'Come on back here, boys.'"

"He wanted you to sweep up or something?" I asked.

"We don't know," Tackett shrugged. "We turned and ran out the front door and into the street."

Benjamin furrowed his brow and regarded both boys with obvious doubt. This didn't surprise me, since Benjamin had been the one most worried all along about getting into trouble. He hadn't even really considered going back to get the Chev out of impoundment, and he'd questioned me about breaking into the boxcar to get the cherries. Maybe he was thinking about the terse lessons his dad had taught him. Clearly he was concerned about the drug store incident.

"So what you're saying, guys," he said, "is that you stole

the smokes?''

''Stole, nothin','' Tackett argued. ''The man tossed 'em to us. He gave them to us. They were free.''

''Yeah,'' Duane said, ''because we'd already explained to him that we didn't have any money.''

''Well,'' I said, ''he must have had some work for you to do in the back room, is all I can think of.''

''If we'd stuck around, though,'' Tackett said, ''we'd have risked missing the train. So which way's better?''

He had me there. After all, I was the one who, just a day earlier, had rationalized breaking into the property of the Great Northern Railroad and stealing two boxes of canned cherries. How could I argue with what Tackett and my brother had done?

''Well then,'' Benjamin said, ''let me ask you this: Did the store keeper chase you down the street?''

''That was the other funny part,'' Duane said, scratching his head. ''We were running real fast and all, but I glanced back about a block away, and I could see the guy standing in the door way. And he was laughing so hard that he was holding his sides. I doubt he could've chased us if he'd tried.''

Benjamin looked at me and I looked at him. Suddenly we both burst out laughing, and then the other two chimed in.

''Well,'' I said, ceremoniously pulling the crumpled cigarette butts from my pocket, ''I guess that means we won't need these anymore.''

I tossed them off the flatcar and we had another good laugh. We each enjoyed a hard-won Lucky and held onto the farm equipment as the train whisked us off toward North Dakota. It would just be a matter of hours now before we made the border, and the excitement was building.

But that wasn't all that was building inside of us. After the day-long digestive cycle with the canned cherries, our systems were left longing again for food -- real food. True: The trip through North Dakota shouldn't take as long as the Montana journey (what could possibly take that long?), but it still would mean a couple of days.

A certain irony suddenly occurred to me as we looked out through the farm equipment at the meandering Missouri. Here we were: practically starving while riding next to the very tools people used to harvest food. But I couldn't think about it for long. It only made me hungrier. And even though we dutifully noted the passage into North Dakota just the other side of Bainville, I wondered what we'd do for food when we got to Williston. I had no way of knowing that the search for food would lead to such an unintentionally hilarious outcome.

Chapter 16

We're in North Dakota!'' Duane exclaimed. ''I can't believe it. I feel like we're almost home.''

''I feel like I'm almost starved for some solid food for a change. I swear if I live to be a hundred years old, I will never, ever, eat canned cherries again. What I could use is some real meat and potatoes type of food.''

I sure could understand how he felt about the cherries. He had gorged himself on them even more-so than the rest of us which had made it neccesary for him to visit the gondola railing much more frequently and for longer durations than the rest of us.

Since, realisticly, meat and potatoes were too much to hope for we decided that some nice fresh vegetables from a local garden would be the next best thing.

So far we'd split up in just about every combination. Since it had grown dark and we were older, Benjamin and I decided we'd be the ones to roam through town and see what we could scare up for the four of us to eat.

''Don't get your hopes up,'' I warned Duane and Tackett. ''We might find some carrots in a vegetable garden, but I wouldn't get your appetite's prepared for anything fancier than that.''

They agreed to stay close to the flatcar, and Benjamin and I assured them we'd be back just as quickly as we could.

The way the town was situated, Benjamin and I figured we'd have our best luck wandering through the alleys behind the store fronts. A lot of the Williston homes had their back yards butting up against the alleys, and we figured the gardens would be easy to find. Williston was about the same size place as Troy had been, meaning it didn't take long to comb the whole town.

After walking half of one alley I thought I saw a vegetable patch barely lit up by the kitchen lights inside of a house.

"You wait here and watch," I said to Benjamin, and I crept into the yard toward the house.

I felt very uneasy about this, unaccustomed as I was to such maneuvers. At least in the case of Farmer Murphy's place I had a ready explanation as to why I was on his property. And I was consoled somewhat with the memory of how well the Murphy episode had turned out. But what if I were to be confronted by a Williston home owner? What could I say in my own defense? I was a common trespasser, after all. They could call the police on me -- or worse.

These thoughts accompanied me as I made my way to the house. Sure enough, a lush truck garden appeared at my feet. But as I bent down to yank some plants, suddenly I heard the loudest, most startling sound I could remember:

"Raugh-r-r-r-roof!"

And there, coming around the side of the house, was an enormous German shepherd. In those days we called them police dogs, which was only too appropriate in this case. I arose and sprinted for the alley, where Benjamin stood frozen. The shepherd chased me with long strides, but just as I passed from the property into the alley he gave up the chase and stood barking and snarling at us. Fortunately he seemed to be trained not to go beyond his own property line. Benjamin and I gingerly walked backward as fast as we could, then turned after about 30 feet and ran to the next block.

"If I wasn't so hungry, this would never be worth it," I said when we'd caught our breath.

We strolled behind a few more store fronts, when Benjamin noticed a light coming from one store. I boosted him up so that he could peer inside.

"Hey," Ron said when he could see, "there's just a guy sitting at a cafe counter reading his paper."

Then I lost my hold on Benjamin and he awkwardly banged his head against the window on his way back down to the alley. That must've alerted the man inside, because when we went around to the front he'd gone out to the alley to investigate. When he came back in, there we were: tattered, tired and very hungry. And we were the only people in the place.

"Somethin' I can get for you boys?" he asked, obviously aware that we weren't local kids.

Here goes nothing again, I thought, and I made my most sincere appeal.

"Sir," I explained, "my friend and I are passing through on the freight train, and we sure haven't eaten very much lately. What we were hoping was that you might have some dishes to wash or floors to sweep or mop -- any chores at all if we could just get a sandwich or something."

"You two kids traveling on the freight train?" he repeated. "Where you boys from?"

"We're from Seattle," I said. "And we're headed for DeLamere, which is by Breckenridge and Wahpeton."

He seemed amazed.

"You kids come all the way out here from Seattle by freight train?"

"Well, most of the way," Ron said. "We started by car, but it didn't work out. Sort of a long story."

He looked us over for a minute, then apparently decided we were telling the truth.

"Okay," he nodded, "then come on in, boys. I'll go back and see if I can scraped something together. Go ahead and take a seat at the counter and I'll be back in a minute."

He wasn't gone long before we heard a sizzling noise that indicated something was frying.

"I think," Ron said, "this means he's not making sandwiches."

"Maybe," I said, "it'll still be something we can wrap up and take with us back to the train."

But I was so hungry that anything at all would've been welcome. He could've given us each some soda crackers and it would've seemed like a feast.

Instead, within minutes he presented us with a genuine feast. He came out of the kitchen with large plates, each of them with a huge fried fish and mashed potatoes and gravy. Then he brought out a pitcher of milk. Oh, lord did everything smell good. And, oh, boy, was it obvious none of it could be wrapped up and transported.

The man then walked to the end of the counter, picked up a stool and brought it back to sit down across the counter from us. He just seemed to welcome having somebody to talk to. Not only were there no other customers, but we could tell there weren't any dirty dishes and the floors didn't need cleaning. It was as though we were the only guests the guy had had all night.

When Ron and I realized there was no chance we could wrap up any of the meal, we just dug in and started eating. I don't know whether it was trout or walleye, but after a bite or two I lost any thoughts of taking it back to the freight yards

-- it was that good.

The man was full of questions.

''How'd you boys decide to take the freights?'' he asked. We told him about the impounding and the quick decision to ride the rail to Ellensburg. Then we took him through the tunnel episode and on to Wenatchee, and how it had just seemed right to keep on going. He followed the story episode by episode, feeling sorry for us when the bad things happened and laughing with us when we admitted doing something funny or stupid -- or both, as was the case with gorging ourselves on canned cherries and getting bellyaches. I realized that sometimes the re-telling of incidents can make them into full-fledged adventures in the minds of the listeners, and this clearly was the case with this man. We could tell he was imagining himself out there with us, running for the trains, grabbing for the ladder rungs, jumping from moving cars and rolling in the gravel beds. Maybe he wished he'd done something like this when he was our age, and maybe he knew his time had passed and he never would get a chance. Thinking about this made me realize how lucky we were -- and how full we were, come to think of it.

We thanked our host, who insisted that we get going and not worry about chores.

''All I ask,'' he laughed, as we headed out the door, ''is that if you make it back this way, do stop in and let me know how everything turned out. Good luck to you.''

We promised that if we did, we'd bring money the next time so that we could pay for such good food.

Then Benjamin and I wandered into the night, patting our bellies and recalling how terrific everything had tasted.

''Of course,'' I reminded him, ''there's one little problem. What do we do about Duane and Tackett? I'd sure feel terrible going back there all full, and not have anything for them.''

"I guess," Benjamin said, "we'll have to just keep searching for a garden, only it's kind of getting a little late."

I was starting to feel bad about being so well fed, knowing that the best the other two guys might get would be raw carrots. We roamed around to the end of an alley, but had no luck spotting any gardens. Then Benjamin saw another restaurant with a light on.

"Maybe this is where we can get take-out food," I suggested, and we crept closer and saw that this second place also was unoccupied -- with the exception of a woman who appeared to be in her early 20s.

"This town has got more empty restaurants," Benjamin said.

"But with this one," I said, "I'm gonna state the matter a little differently. This time I'll just say 'sandwiches to take with us,' and maybe that's what she'll give us. That is, if we can get anything at all."

When we entered, however, it soon occurred to me that I wasn't going to be doing much of the talking anyway. I'd known Ron Benjamin long enough to be able to tell when he was taken with a young woman, and as soon as he fixed his gaze on the attractive waitress he took the initiative in explaining our predicament. I didn't even try to get a word in edgewise, as Benjamin finished a brief account of where we'd come from by asking:

"Do you think there's any chance you could spare us each a couple of slices of bread and some cold cuts or peanut butter? Anything would be great: leftovers from lunch, maybe."

She seemed concerned for us. And of course she had no way of knowing that all we really wanted was something to take back to the other boys.

"You boys go get comfortable in a booth," she finally said, turning toward the kitchen. "I'll go back to the kitchen and see what I can find for you. I think I just might have some roast pork back there."

When she disappeared I rolled my eyes and said: "Oh, lord, Ron. Now what have we gotten ourselves into?"

"We're too pathetic for our own good, I guess," he sighed, and both of us thought of our full bellies again. "But I'll say this, Jerry. She sure is pretty, isn't she?"

I shrugged in a way to suggest that maybe getting the food out of the restaurant was a more pressing matter.

"Maybe," I said, "she'll make roast pork sandwiches that we can carry out."

Within minutes I saw just how wrong I was. She brought us each a full meal, with this one even more elaborate than the fish dinners had been. Then she turned and headed back to the kitchen, and once again Benjamin said: "Yep, she's sure better looking than our last host."

"Well," I said, "I can see we've got a problem here. How are we gonna get any of this grub out of here?"

But as we hestitated to dig in the waitress returned with glasses of milk.

"Oh," she quickly said when she thought Benjamin and I might just be trying to be polite, "I know you're starved, so you don't have to use your best manners on my account. Go ahead and dig in with both hands. That's what it's there for."

But all I could think about was that huge fish dinner of half an hour earlier. And after half a meal of roast pork, mashed potatoes and vegetables we could barely bring ourselves to put the forks in our mouths, let alone chew. I kept hoping our hostess would get up and head back to the kitchen. Then maybe I could slip some meat into my pocket. But then I realized that it wouldn't be worth eating in such condition.

And after we'd made such a big deal about how starved we were after our long trip, what choice did we have but to keep eating?

I thought maybe I could keep myself from having to shovel in the grub by telling our hostess what by now was an only too familiar story. I took her through the sequences of the adventure, and she followed up with lots of questions: What had we enjoyed the most on the trip so far? What did we do for fun back in Seattle? We were the only customers and it was undoubtedly a good feeling for her just to have somebody to talk with, especially two people from as far away as Seattle.

Finally Benjamin and I stopped eating and patted our bellies again. We wanted to indicate that we'd had our fill and could eat no more, but the waitress must've taken it as a sign that we were trying to be polite again. She had no way of knowing the truth.

"Would you like some more?" She asked as she started to get up.

"Oh no!" I answered quickly, "We're stuffed. We really are. I couldn't eat another bite. Really I couldn't."

"Me neither," Ron put in.

"Well, okay," she said, "but you're welcome to more if you wish."

In little more than an hour our systems had gone from little food to more than we'd ever consumed in such a brief time, and I still don't know how we did it. My greatest fear was that my stomach wasn't going to be able to hold all this food and that I would lose it right in front of them. Several times I had to stifle a belch, and I could feel that my face was almost as bloated as my belly. It didn't serve to speculate about what it was doing to my digestive system with all this food being introduced to a starved, empty stomach. The way my belly felt, it couldn't have been good, because Benjamin and I had long since gone far beyond the point of feeling well fed. Now we were about to explode.

I thought for a moment that there was going to be a bad accident if we didn't get a move on, and I grabbed Benjamin by the arm and hastened him to the door. We managed to get outside after thanking the waitress for such a great meal. I felt as though we'd escaped, and I hoped Ron would hurry along with me in case she came following us with another note like the one Alice Murphy had given Ron.

But no such gesture came this time and Ron seemed a little disappointed.

"Thought maybe I'd pick up another pen pal, Jerry," he said. "But I guess one's plenty for a guy with a girlfriend waiting back home."

But he and I both knew that his girl encounters were the least of our problems just now.

Chapter 17

It was so late by now that we knew Duane and Tackett would be worried about us. I suppose we could've groped around in the dark of Williston for another half hour, but Benjamin and I were both so full that we could hardly move. We knew we needed to just get back to the flatcar and make the best of it.

"The trouble is, Ron," I said, "is that I just don't have the heart to tell those guys what happened."

"Heart, nothin'," Benjamin said. "I haven't got the nerve to tell them. Think of it if the situation was reversed. Those guys are back there with empty bellies and we're so full we can hardly walk."

I knew it was going to be an interesting confrontation once we got back to the flatcar.

"What bothers me most, I guess," I admitted, "is that I can just about bet my brother would have found some way to get that food out of the restaurant and back to us."

"I sure don't know how," Benjamin sighed, as we rounded the last corner of town and slowly headed toward the rail yards. "It's pretty hard to slip gloppy mashed potatoes into your pocket. That fish we had at the first place wouldn't have been worth eating after riding around in my pants."

''And I guess,'' I agreed, ''it would've been awfully rude to ask for some bread slices to make sandwiches out of the pork.''

Benjamin belched a good one.

''Boy,'' he said, ''I'm just glad there aren't anymore restaurants in Williston. I don't know if I'll ever be able to eat again.''

I guess we sort of concluded that we'd asked for it. Maybe if we'd been perfectly honest with the restaurant people and told them about the boys back at the flatcar, then maybe we'd have gotten what we needed. Or it could be it would've been better after the first meal to go back to the train and let the other two guys go into town and scare up something. But you never know about these things until the possibility already has come and gone.

''Ron,'' I said, ''I think you and I both know we've got to somehow keep from telling Duane and Tackett what happened. If we tell 'em they'll never speak to us again.''

Benjamin stifled another belch and said: ''I just don't know if that's gonna be possible, Jerry.''

But we conspired anyway. Within a few minutes we'd gotten back to the flatcar, where the greeting from Duane and Tackett was less than enthusiastic. It was as though they guessed that we didn't have anything for them, even though they couldn't tell in the dark that we were bloated like pigs.

I decided to break the bad news as quickly as possible. Duane searched my face for positive signs, but in the dim light of the railroad yard all he could see was my shrug.

''Sorry, guys,'' I said, barely able to keep from burping. ''Me and Ron . . . well . . .''

Then Benjamin said: ''We looked all over town, all right. Jerry here just about gotten eaten by a police dog near somebody's vegetable patch. Nah, the town's dead, all right.

It appears as though we'll have to get to DeLamere before we can get something to eat.''

Duane shrugged and seemed almost apologetic all of a sudden. ''Well,'' he said, ''I guess Tackett and I did better than you two, then, but not by much.''

He walked back to the flatcar and returned with a can in his hand.

''Tackett and I got some food while you were gone, all right. It's nothin' but a can of cold corn, but we only ate half of it. Saved the rest for you.''

''This hobo came by,'' Tackett explained, ''and we got to gabbin' with him, and when we told him we hadn't eaten for a while he pulled a can of corn out of his grip and just gave it to us.''

''Just like that,'' Duane added. ''Like I say, it isn't very fancy, but it's yours if you want it. You poor guys gotta be ready to eat something, I guess.''

Suddenly I didn't feel the least bit well as I got a distinct whiff of the aroma from the cold canned corn. It would've smelled rank under the best of circumstances, but coming along after all we'd eaten it smelled downright threatening to me. I glanced nervously over toward Benjamin, who if anything had eaten more than I had during the pair of feasts that evening. Even in the dim light I could make out his slightly pained expression. This was the last thing either of us expected would happen.

''Yeah,'' Tackett said. ''It's no feast, that's for sure. But I guess it's better than canned cherries. At least this stuff will stick with a guy for more than a few hours.''

I checked the expression on Benjamin's face and could tell he was thinking along the lines I was: Here we were, stuffed on two meals, unable to share our feasts. And here were the other guys: darned near apologizing to us for only being able to offer cold corn.

Duane seemed a little surprised that Benjamin and I hadn't said anything. More than anything else, I wished somehow that can of corn would slip out of Duane's fingers and the niblets would spill out into the dirt where nobody could be forced to eat them.

He shoved the can Benjamin's way, but Ron was quicker on his feet than I was.

"Yuck," Benjamin said, with an expression of disgust that I could identify with. "I hate cold canned corn."

Then I really knew I was in for it. If I'd have been thinking, then I could've been the one to express my disdain for the corn. But Benjamin had beaten me to the punch, and now I was in a jam.

Duane offered me the can. I accepted it and just stood there, staring down at those pale niblets. If I refused to eat, then I risked letting on what had happened with Benjamin and me in town. A few minutes earlier the confession would've been all right. But by now we'd lied to Duane and Tackett, and we had to stick with our story.

And my gut was really feeling the effects of the two dinners by now. It nearly made me sick just to think about eating the corn niblets, and I couldn't imagine what would happen if I actually ate them. I was almost certain I'd throw up the whole mess, revealing just exactly how full my stomach actually had been. Then I'd really have some explaining to do.

I raised the container and thought I'd maybe just pretend in the dim light to take a bite. Instead, a couple of niblets slipped into my mouth. After what I'd consumed that night they tasted like pellets of poison. I gummed the corn but couldn't swallow. I let the niblets slip unseen back into the can, then pulled the container away and said:

"Double yuck! This cold corn just doesn't make it. I don't care how hungry I get."

I handed the can back to Duane and waited to see how well my act had gone over. But he took the can back to the flatcar and set it down again, apparently sorrier than ever that it was all he and Tackett could offer. My stomach was relieved, but my conscience felt worse than ever.

But Duane eased my guilt a little by letting on that he apparently didn't care for cold corn for dinner anymore than we did. Maybe if there'd been some way to heat it up we could've made it palatable.

"I guess we're just not full-fledged hoboes yet," Duane concluded. "The fellow who gave us the corn acted like he was handing us a real first-class feast."

"Maybe you just have to be starving a little more before this stuff starts to taste good," I suggested, visualizing how much my brother and Tackett would've loved sharing in our restaurant feasts.

It was so late now that there was little to do but get our bedding ready for the night's sleep. Benjamin and I had to work to keep from groaning as we lay down, happy to be resting our bellies. At one point I actually let out an involuntary belch again, and covered it by muttering something about the canned corn.

There was a lot of racket in the rail yard that night, and it kept us awake a long time. We passed the time talking about what we'd do first when we got to DeLamere.

"Sleep in a bed?" Duane suggested.

"Write a letter to Gay, maybe," Benjamin said.

"And maybe another one to Alice Murphy," Tackett added, playfully.

I wasn't sure just what I'd do. I still had no way of gauging how we'd be greeted by Dad. Would he be glad to see us? Would we be a bother to him?

"I guess," I said, "that I'll also have to write a letter and let Mom know what happened. Assuming I can remember everything."

"Well," Tackett said, "it ain't over yet, either."

"No," I granted, "we've still got a few hundred more miles until it ends. Judging from all the people we've met so far, anything could still be waiting to happen out there."

Duane and Tackett then took some time to tell us about their encounter with the hobo. It occurred to me that, for all the warnings we'd heard about what a bunch of desperadoes these rail riders were, the two we'd actually encountered hadn't really been bad sorts. They just seemed to be fellows who, for one reason or another, didn't want the responsibilities most folks have. Riding the rails gave them all the freedom they needed. If they could keep food in their mouths and clothes on their backs, then what else did they really need?

"This hobo," Duane was saying, "he sounded like he's led quite a life."

Tackett said: "He sure did. This guy told about all his scrapes with the police and how many places he'd been. He said he'd ridden trains in all 48 states and most of Canada. I guess he never gets tired of it."

And as he said this it occurred to me maybe I would get tired of it someday soon. It was true that the exhilaration still existed for me every time I felt the wind in my face as we rode across the prairie. Nobody could deny the pure fun of knowing you could hop a freight and travel freely half way across the country. But I had to believe it would get monotonous after a while. Pretty soon the novelty would wear off and you'd just be riding for the sake of moving, for the sake of avoiding putting down roots.

For a boy of 17, though, it had proven to be something of a rite of passage. I couldn't express it that way at the time because the boys and I still lacked a lot of the life experience we'd gain in the years to come. I guess it was more that I just felt something had changed inside of me. I'd gained confidence. I had a heightened sense of being able to take care of myself and see to it things got done. In a way, by supposedly being irresponsible during this wonderful summer of 1948, I'd actually learned how to be responsible, not just for myself but for the other boys.

"Anyway," Tackett said, "this hobo said something about wanting to settle down some day."

"In a warm climate," Duane added.

"Says he has family scattered everywhere, but he never really sees any of them," Tackett said. "He thought maybe he'd open up a shoe store. He'd worked selling shoes once I guess."

"People will always need shoes, he said to us," Duane noted. "I guess he's not half wrong about that."

"And they'll always need boots, too," Tackett added, looking my way with a grin that told me he'd forgiven me for the incident in Troy.

With that, Duane got deep into the sleeping bag and fished around to see that his own shoes were where he'd left them next to the bag. After having lost the bundles, we'd taken to trading off with the bag and it was Duane's turn. He didn't want to stick his dusty shoes down into the bag. The rest of us just pulled a blanket over us the best we could, happy that this time of year it wouldn't get too cold at night. The thought of a soft mattress and a quiet night's sleep suddenly seemed very appealing to me, and I took this as yet another sign that we were moving toward the end of the adventure. For a while none of us said anything as we lay there gazing up at the stars.

It seemed that no matter how far you traveled the constellations always looked pretty much the same. It had me thinking back to the feeling I'd had a few days earlier, when I'd observed that you're never very far from home because the center of the world always is where you happen to be at the time.

The train started with its familiar jolt and I imagine we all felt happy that we'd be moving on again. Williston had been the most memorable stop of the adventure, if only from a food standpoint. So close now to Breckenridge, I knew there wouldn't be many more hours of train ride left for us. It was best to just enjoy it while we could, because unless we ever decided to become real hoboes we'd likely never get a chance to do this again. Society seemed to get a kick out of the idea of teenage boys hopping freights to go see their dad. But the world didn't reserve those same warm feelings for grownups who were hoboes -- or ''bums,'' as they were often called.

So it was with mixed emotions that I finally drifted off to sleep, lulled by the swaying of the flatcar and the fragrances of the night. It was just loud enough so that any snores or sleeping sounds were drowned out. But it wasn't loud enough to muffle the sound of a 15-year-old boy suddenly awakened to make a terrifying discovery. It was Duane's voice calling out in the middle of the night. Given my history of dreaming, I wasn't even sure for a moment whether it was really happening or whether it was just one more thing my mind had imagined. But then I realized it really was Duane yelling, saying:

''Hey! This isn't funny. Which one of you guys took my shoes?''

Chapter 18

In the morning everybody pitied Duane, and why not? For a few frantic minutes the night before we'd scrambled around the flatcar, searching in vain for my brother's shoes. We'd assured him until we were blue in the face that none of us had anything to do with the lost shoes. I think Duane knew we weren't kidding him, but he wanted so much for there to be a logical explanation for the disappearance that he kept checking back.

"You guys sure you didn't hide the shoes?" he'd say.

"Duane," I'd answer, "of course we're sure."

Then we'd check around again and he'd say: "You sure you're sure?"

"Duane," Tackett had answered, "where would we have hidden them? There's only so much room on this danged flatcar. We've searched everything six times. Besides, do you think we'd deliberately want to get up out of bed and look for your shoes if we didn't have to?"

"Face it, Duane," Benjamin had concluded, still bloated and weary from his dual dinners, "your shoes are gone. Either they blew off or flew away when the train bolted out of here or . . ."

Or the other alternative: Some nimble-fingered hobo had

grabbed them in the blackness just after we'd bedded down and right before the train had pulled out. By the time the discovery was made our train was in high gear, flying along the North Dakota prairie in the dark of night.

"Some thievin' hobo," Tackett had concluded, solemnly. "Probably the same one that gave us the corn. Serves us right for thinkin' we'd ever get somethin' for nothin'."

"Except," Duane had said, obviously getting more upset the more he thought about it, "I believe I'd have rather kept the shoes and let him keep the corn."

"I'll second that," Benjamin had offered, and it occurred to me my brother and Tackett still didn't know about our feasts. Maybe Benjamin was pressing our luck a little.

The missing shoes continued to be the main topic of conversation in the morning, when we arose somewhere in central North Dakota.

"I hope those shoes are about a size and a half too small for that hobo," Duane asserted

"If they are," Tackett said, "he'll probably just swap 'em with some other bum. That's the way they work it, I'll bet."

"The basic problem," I said, "is that Duane's got nothing to wear on his feet and we're still a good 300 miles from Dad's. If I hadn't accidentally ditched Tackett's cowboy boots, we'd at least have a spare pair to get us by."

But we didn't. And we had no money to buy Duane any foot wear.

"Maybe," Benjamin suggested, "the best thing to do would be for us to get off in the next little town and see what we can scare up. Could be there's a second-hand store where we could swap something for a pair of old shoes."

"Swap what?" Duane demanded.

"Well," I said, "I could hock my watch."

"That old Timex?" Tackett scoffed. "Wouldn't bring you enough for a couple packs of smokes."

He was probably right. Even if I could've pawned the watch, none of the towns in this part of North Dakota was anywhere big enough to have a hock shop. And I'd never pawned anything anyway. I wasn't even sure whether a 17-year-old kid was allowed to hock something.

No, we had to face the fact that we'd be living bare bones from here on to DeLamere.

"Besides," Duane concluded, "there's no real point getting off the train now. We're rolling along real good now, so we'd best just stay on and make as much progress as we can. Then, when we get to DeLamere, my dad can buy me some new shoes."

I wasn't altogether sure of that. The closer we got to our destination, the more I wondered just exactly how we'd be received. Here was Dad: back in his old home town, minding his own business. DeLamere was so small that you could go days without ever even talking with anybody. Dad probably had little communication with the outside world. He no doubt spent his days working the property, never even dreaming two of his sons and their friends might show up unannounced at his front door some day.

What if Dad somehow was angry about the adventure? The possibility at least existed. Maybe the trip to North Dakota had been a bad idea from the start. I started to wonder what it might've been like had the car not been impounded. The boys and I by now would've gotten well established in Ellensburg. In a week's time we surely would've found work and maybe even gotten a place to stay. Even without the car, if we'd thumbed from Wenatchee to Peshastin and down to Ellensburg we'd already have a fews days work in.

And the money. I started calculating. If we'd made 75 cents an hour and worked steadily, then maybe we'd have put together $6 a day each. That would've meant as much as $150 or better by now -- maybe 40 bucks each. Why, with that kind of dough we could've lived like kings. There'd have been plenty for food, and maybe even a place to stay. We could've afforded to buy some fenders, grab a bus ride back to Skykomish, get the car out of impoundment and undo the whole mess.

And if we worked another week or so, then each of us might have a hundred bucks. Just think of what that would buy back in Seattle. We could help out Mom with grocery money and still have spending loot leftover for the rest of the summer.

Yeah, I thought, that would've been the safe way to play things all right. But would it have been as much fun as the adventure? Not a chance. What money could buy experiences such as the ones we'd had? If we'd have gone to Ellensburg and picked potatoes, I have no doubt we would have amassed lots of great memories to carry with us. But I know none of them ever would've stuck with us as long as these adventures.

Besides, there was still the possibility that we could make some money in DeLamere. We'd probably have to if we ever planned to get back to Seattle. I thought of the old neighborhood in Seattle, wondering what it would feel like getting back to the old block after so much had happened.

But for now we had priorities that interrupted my daydreams. During the night the train had covered a lot of North Dakota, clacking along through Minot and drawing down through Rugby toward Devil's Lake. After a brief stop there in late morning we beat it for Valley City. The two younger boys remained pretty hungry, since all they'd eaten in two days was cherries and corn. As for Benjamin and me, we'd long since run out of cigarettes. If nothing else, I thought, as the train slowed down and eased into Valley City in the late afternoon, we could kill the time during the layover kicking around for cigarette butts to last us the rest of the trip.

Duane shuffled over to the nearby woods to relieve himself while the two Rons and I scuffed about the railroad yard. Down toward the end of the train I could see that a brakeman was watching us with great interest.

"Don't look now," I said to the others, "but we've got an audience."

It was the first time the whole trip that we'd felt conspicuous in a railroad yard. Ever since that first arrival in Wenatchee we'd let ourselves just blend in with the train-yard activity, and it had worked well for us.

"What d'ya suppose he wants?" Tackett said, as we gradually maneuvered out of his line of sight and back toward the woods.

"Probably wonders why anybody would be caught dead in such a god-forsaken place as this," Benjamin speculated.

Just then Duane came out of the woods. He was carrying a stout stick in one hand.

"Found my missing five-iron in the woods," he grinned.

Duane was a great one for games. He'd managed to find what might've been some hobo's walking stick, which was about four feet long with a crook at the end. From a distance it really did look kind of like a golf club.

"As long as we're looking for smokes," Duane proposed, "let's gather up some rocks about golf ball size and we can have a tournament once the train takes off."

It sounded like something to take our minds off of our problems. We also were so close to Breckenridge now that we were getting antsy. We gathered up a bunch of rocks and found some more choice butts. Pretty soon the train pulled out with us four hoboes back on our flatcar.

"Boy," I said, "do you guys realize we're only a few stops away?"

"I never even thought about actually arriving," Benjamin said. "So far all I've thought about was the fun of traveling."

But Duane was prepared to help get our minds off of the trip for a while. He was always a great competitor, Duane. He had a terrific golf swing, which would serve him well later in life. And there he was: standing on that open flatcar, swatting make-believe golf balls off the platform and out through the evening sky. The rest of us would take a turn, and we'd all laugh and joke. I think the younger two kids had finally gone beyond being hungry. Somehow growing boys seem to be able to summon the energy it takes to do what seems like fun at the time. Besides, we all knew that we wouldn't ultimately starve to death. Even if Dad wasn't thrilled with what we'd done, he'd at least see to it we were well fed.

He would, that is, assuming we made it to DeLamere. Suddenly that was in question, as Tackett glanced ahead of us amid the fun we were having and said:

"Uh, fellas, I think we have some company."

Making his way over the boxcars up ahead of us was the brakeman who'd seen us in the yard.

"Gosh," Benjamin shouted, "what should we do?"

"Run?" Duane yelled.

"We can't jump," I said, "because we're going too fast. We better wait and see what we're in for."

Now the brakeman was pointing at us as though to say: "Don't you boys dare try to run."

"I think he's mad," Tackett said, knowing it was an understatement.

Then the brakeman was climbing down the adjacent boxcar, crossing over the coupling and standing on our flatcar.

"You're the boys I saw in the yard at Valley City," he said, clearly perturbed.

"Yes sir," I said. "Have we done something wrong?"

He looked me over and said: "Not if you think it's all right to hop a free ride on a freight train you haven't."

"Well," I stammered, "uh, pardon me sir, but maybe I can explain."

But he waved a hand, indicating maybe I'd better not.

"You kids realize it's a dangerous crime to let debris go flying off a train like this?"

"We were just having a little fun," Duane said. "It was my idea. We were pretending to be golfers."

"Golfers, eh," the brakeman said. "What kind of kids would ride a train out through the middle of North Dakota to pretend like golfers? I have half a mind to stop this train right here and kick you boys off. You can walk to where ever you're going."

Then he looked down at Duane's bare feet.

"You," he said. "Barefoot boy with cheeks of tan. You won't get very far walking with no shoes, will you."

He turned and started back. I was sure he was going to stop the train, so I figured I better speak my mind.

"Mister," I said, "the truth is that we've come half way across the country from Seattle. We've had lots of bad luck and a little good luck, but lately we haven't had enough to eat and maybe we're not thinking straight. But we're good kids. We haven't been in any trouble. It's just that my dad lives not far from Breckenridge and we've been traveling day and night to get to his place. If you could somehow find it in you to let us stay aboard for a while longer, we'll promise not to do anything wrong. Besides, it's getting pretty late now. Please don't make us get off the train.''

He looked each one of us up one end and down the other, never smiling at any of us. Then he spoke.

''I'm going to give you four kids a little advice,'' he said. ''Somebody needs to teach you a lesson about hopping freight trains. In the first place, it isn't safe. In the second place, you run into some pretty hard characters.''

He'd told us two things we already knew.

''Besides that,'' he said, ''it's against the law.''

With that he turned and climbed to the top of the boxcar.

''Now I'm not going to stop this train and kick you boys off,'' he said, and my heart soared. ''It's not worth disrupting the schedule to do that.''

We could hardly contain ourselves.

But then he added: ''What I am going to do is kick you kids off at the very next stop along the way.''

Our spirits sank again.

''Now don't you kids try to talk me out of it, either,'' the brakeman said. ''You're getting off the second this train comes to a full stop. And I don't want you boys hanging around the train station hoping to catch another freight, either, hear me?''

We nodded as the brakeman turned and headed back to where he'd been. Suddenly DeLamere seemed a lot farther away than the crow-fly distance that it was.

And then, in the distance, we heard the brakeman's voice again. He seemed to be repeating what he'd said earlier and I thought: ''C'mon, mister, we already feel bad enough as it is.''

But what he said made us feel a whole lot better. He shouted back to us:

''Yeah, you're getting off the train the next stop, all right.

Fortunately for you four, the next stop is Breckenridge, Minnesota.''

Chapter 19

I lit a match so I could check my watch. It was 3:15 in the morning. None of us had slept more than a wink all night. This was it! We were arriving in Breckenridge, Minnesota. Hallelujah! We'd just about come to the end of our journey.

We made sure that all our gear was bundled up properly for dismounting the train and traveling the final 35 miles.

"This is it guys," I said. "The train is slowing down. When it gets down to a safe speed we'll just step off and walk over to that street."

I gestured into the night, where a lonely looking street was barely lit under some street lights. The street led to a bridge.

"That's the way to go to get back into North Dakota," I said.

It was almost as though the engineer had us in mind when he pulled off the mainline track and onto a secondary track. He was moving along at a speed that made it easy for us to step off long before the train came to a stop, thereby leaving us the least possible distance to walk to the main street of Breckenridge.

We were euphoric.

"How's this for service?" Duane exclaimed. We were

here. We'd made it 1,500 miles without sustaining any serious setbacks. Looking back on it, I guess I didn't think we ever really doubted we could make it. It was just that it had been such a novel experience for us that we had no way of knowing how long it would take or how much hardship we'd have to suffer.

We stepped onto the sidewalk of the main street of town and started walking back toward the west. I realized that the easternmost point of our journey was finally behind us. Ahead of us was North Dakota, which we entered after passing over the bridge that spans the Red River. The river separates Breckenridge from Wahpeton, North Dakota.

At that time of early morning we might have figured to be alone for another hour or so before the local activity gradually brought Wahpeton to life. But just after we passed into Wahpeton a police car swung past us, heading in the same direction. Then it pulled forward a ways and abruptly took a U turn. I sensed this might mean trouble, but then I wondered: Why should it?

"My god," Benjamin groaned to nobody in particular, "what did we do this time?"

The cop car came to a stop at the curb next to us. We stopped and the officer sized us up for a moment from inside the car. Since we didn't move he finally got out and walked around the car to confront us.

"You kids aren't from around here, are you?" he said, less as a question than a statement.

"No, sir," I said. "We're from Seattle."

"Seattle?" he repeated. "All four of you from way out in Seattle? And you just happen to be roaming around here in Wahpeton in the middle of the night?"

I had to admit to myself that it did sound a little unlikely.

"Well," I said, "we didn't plan to be here this time of

night, but that's when the freight train stopped in Breckenridge.''

"The freight train?'' he repeated. ''You mean to tell me you four came all the way out from Seattle by freight? Just you four kids alone?''

"Yessir, we sure did,'' I said, and suddenly I felt very proud of the accomplishment. There was no point hiding the fact that we'd ridden the rails. After all, now that we had done it there wasn't anything anybody could do to us. We'd gotten away with it, and now there was every reason to feel proud of ourselves. Not only that but there wasn't any curfew. There was no reason to feel guilty about anything, I realized, so I figured I'd just tell the officer where we stood.

"And what do your folks think about all of this?'' he wanted to know.

"Well,'' I said, ''that's the whole thing about this trip. We're going to see my dad in DeLamere. It's about 30--''

"Oh, I know where DeLamere is,'' the officer said. ''Does your dad know you kids are traveling 1,500 miles cross country on a freight train to come see him?''

Suddenly that seemed to be a central question of the entire adventure. And it seemed a little late to be thinking about the consequences if it proved Dad either would object to what we'd done or -- who really knew? -- had gone away from DeLamere. What if we showed up in the little town only to find that Dad was away?

"Uh, no sir,'' I said. ''See, we were going to surprise him.''

The officer grinned just a little. ''Oh,'' he said, ''I have no doubt that you'll surprise him, all right: four kids show up unannounced at your front door early in the morning.''

The officer looked each of us over, with his gaze finally settling on Duane's bare feet. He looked up at Duane's face, then skeptically glanced down at his feet again.

''Son,'' he said, ''you didn't come all the way from Seattle like that, did you?''

''Oh, no, sir,'' Duane said. ''Only the last 300 miles. Some hobo swiped my shoes off me back in Williston. At least I think that's what happened.''

The cop shook his head. ''I guess I don't even dare ask how you wouldn't know for sure whether a hobo swiped your own shoes off you.''

''It happened while we were sleeping,'' I explained. ''My brother had taken off the shoes to get comfortable.''

''Bet you ain't quite so comfortable now,'' the officer said to Duane, adding: ''Don't this just beat all? How are you expecting to get to DeLamere?''

''Well,'' I said, ''we figured on hitchhiking, but if we can't get a ride I guess we'll just have to walk.''

The cop was skeptical again. ''You figure this kid here is going to walk 35 miles on a gravel road barefooted?''

Once again, it sounded as unlikely as the adventure itself.

''Well,'' Duane assured the cop, ''I've got pretty tough feet. I used to go barefoot a lot. Besides, after what we've been through this past week, I don't think even a bed of nails could stop me.''

Now it occurred to me that the officer was starting to admire us for our spunk.

''Well, boys,'' he said, ''I sure don't have any reason to hold you, so about all I can do is wish you luck.''

Then he looked over at Duane again and down to his bare feet.

''And son,'' he said, ''I especially wish you luck.''

With that he drove off, and we headed off down the main drag of Wahpeton and off toward the other end of town. Highway 13 was the road that led toward DeLamere.

"Highway 13," Tackett noted. "Hope that's a lucky number for us."

By now we were at the edge of town. A breakfast diner had opened for early business, and we looked through the window longing for something to eat. Dead broke, we also were out of smokes.

"What I wouldn't give for one of Alice Murphy's sandwiches right now," Duane sighed.

"Yeah," Tackett said, then turned to Benjamin and asked: "And by the way, Ron, what did Alice say in that love letter she gave you?"

Benjamin said: "It wasn't any love letter. It just gave her address and said she wants us to let her know what happened to us."

"Seems like a small price for all those sandwiches," I said, but Tackett seemed unconvinced and Benjamin knew it.

"Well," Benjamin finally said, reaching for his wallet, "if you don't believe me, read it yourself."

He fumbled around in his billfold, then suddenly his eyes shone in amazement in the early morning light. Then he pulled something from his billfold, and it wasn't a letter.

"Look at this, guys!" he exclaimed. "All this time I had a buck tucked back in my secret compartment."

Sure enough, it was a small fortune under the circumstances. It bought us some smokes and candy bars, and no candy bar before or since ever tasted so good.

But if the discovery of Highway 13 had proved lucky in that sense, the road was decidedly unlucky for Duane. We had to walk fairly slowly through the matted gravel, because Duane was walking along the shoulder in the rough grass and brush. While this was easier on his feet, occasionally he'd step on a cockleburr or thistle and let out a pained "yowch!" Then we'd have to stop for a while so he could sit down, pull out the stickers and rub the soreness out of his feet. Then we'd start up again, though I wasn't sure how much more of this Duane would be able to take. If his feet started seriously bleeding, then we'd really have a mess to deal with.

In 1948 there wasn't any national daylight-savings time, so by 4:30 in the morning in late July it was already getting pretty light out. After about two hours of slow progress, only two vehicles had passed us, neither driver giving us the time of day. We decided to rest along the side of the road, and for that Duane was grateful -- even though he gamely wanted to continue. But I could tell how sore he was, and when an old pickup truck finally rumbled past us Duane and Tackett stayed down while Benjamin and I stood up and stuck out our thumbs.

''For all the good this'll do,'' Benjamin said.

But I looked ahead after the truck passed and it appeared it was slowing down.

''Holy cow, he's stopping,'' I shouted. ''Get up, you guys.''

After all we'd been through, it occurred to me that this was our first actual ride from hitchhiking. I pulled open the front door and hopped in while the other guys threw the gear into the truck bed and climbed aboard.

''We sure appreciate this, sir,'' I said. ''Especially my brother. He's walking barefoot.''

I looked back through the rear window to see that the other three were okay, then asked the driver hopefully:

''How far you going?'' ''Goin' to Milner,'' he said. ''At least almost that far. I live about two miles this side.''

''Boy, that's great,'' I said. We've only got to get as far as DeLamere or thereabouts. We don't know for sure where the farm is that my dad's living on, but it's somewhere around there.''

"What's you pa's name, son?" the driver asked.

"Vic Jacobson," I answered.

"Vic?" he repeated. "I know Vic. All you boys his sons?"

"Oh, no, sir, just me and Duane, the barefoot kid. The other two fellows are just friends of ours. We just got off the train in Breckenridge. Took it all the way out here from Seattle."

He looked a little puzzled. "On the train? And not even one suitcase between you?"

"Well, uh," I said, "We didn't travel on the passenger train. We rode the freights all the way."

He looked at me with a funny expression. "You don't say?" he marveled. "The four of you, all that way?"

"No kidding," I said, and suddenly I felt less like a kid telling something to a grownup, more as though I was talking man to man. "I think it took us eight days, but I sort of lost track."

"Well, I do declare," he said. "If that ain't something. I'd sure welcome hearing all about it some day. I bet it was a real experience -- somethin' boys don't just get up and do every day."

"Yes," I said, "It sure was an experience, all right. Some day maybe I'll sit down and write a book about it."

And upon saying so, I realized maybe I just would some day write about it at that.

"Son," the driver said, after we'd driven quite a ways through the North Dakota countryside, "your pa lives out on the old Tranksrud place. It's about two miles out of DeLamere, only about a mile off the main road."

In a while we turned off on an old dirt road, and when we reached a driveway leading into a grove of trees he pulled to a stop.

"I'll just let you boys out here," the driver said. "That way you can walk up and really surprise your old man."

The other three climbed out and grabbed the gear, and each of us went up to the driver's window and thanked him heartily for what he'd done for us.

"Glad to help you boys," the driver laughed as he drove off.

It was just about mid-morning by now. The driveway into the farm was about a hundred yards or so. We were so close to Dad now that I wasn't even thinking about what his reaction would be. It was best to just find him and surprise him.

As we rounded the corner after the last few trees, we suddenly saw a hulk emerging from a lean-to at the side of the barn. It was Dad, all right. He'd been feeding the chickens that he kept in the lean-to. They were the only animals that he kept on the farm.

Dad stopped dead in his tracks when he saw us, and stood there for a few seconds. Then he slowly walked toward us.

"Duane?" he spoke incredulously. "Gerald?" He always called me by my given name. "Is it really you?"

Then in an instant the three of us were hugging, and in that moment there was no need for any explanation. We broke from the hugs and we could see it was taking time to sink in.

"What are you two doing here?" Dad wanted to know. "How in the world could you have gotten here?"

Then I realized just how good a question this was.

"Dad," I grinned, "it's too long of a story to tell while we're standing up. Let's go inside."

"I don't suppose you kids have had any breakfast," he said. "Are you boys hungry?"

Each of us looked at him, then we looked at each other, as if to say: "Is he kidding?"

It took Duane to put it into words.

"Dad," he asked, "does a cat have eyes?"

With that, we all laughed and walked inside, and had the first good, hot breakfast at a real table that we'd had since . . ah . . . since . . . ah . . .

That's all there is,
        (That's all there is),
There ain't no more,
        (There ain't no more),
Saint Peter said
        (Saint Peter said)
When he closed that door.
        (When he closed that door).

Oh, yes, that's all there is,
There ain't no more,
Saint Peter said
When he closed that door.
I ain't gonna grieve, my lord no more,
I ain't gonna grieve, my lord no more,
I ain't gonna grieve, my lord no more,
I ain't gonna grie-e-e-ve, my lord no more.

THE END

Epilogue

When the summer was over we returned to Seattle, again using the freight trains of the Great Northern R. R. as our means of transportation. It turned out to be the most memorable summer of our lives. An adventure that few teenage boys ever have the opportunity to experience.

When his school days were over, Ron Tackett, the youngest of our group became a plumber. He married young and he and his wife, Arlene have raised five children, eleven grandchildren and two great grandchildren. They now live in Henderson, Nevada where he has a plumbing business.

Ron Benjamin, following in his fathers footsteps, became a sheet metal worker. After receiving Ron's postcard about the car impounding his father and uncle went to Skykomish and retrieved the car. It was an unpopular subject in the Benjamin household for quite some time. Ron now lives in southern California.

I never did get over my desire to see what's on the other side of the hill. My uncle Oscar always called me 'Ole Itchyfoot'. But I found a girl who also liked to see new places and in the forty years that we have been married we have lived in Japan, Washington, California, Alaska, Hawaii and Florida. We now reside in Marysville, Wa.

Duane's golfing ability and his easy way of dealing with the public landed him a job as a pro-manager of a public golf course in Snohomish, Wa.

Duane had two sons. When the youngest son was 14 years old he ran away from home. For two days Duane and his wife were frantic. On the third day they received a call from the police in Bend, Or.

"We have a young man here by the name of Gary Jacobson who says he belongs to you. Is that right?"

"Yes" my brother said, "but what has he done?"

"Nothing illegal, "the officer answered, "but he's only 14 years old and we found him roaming the streets at 3 in the morning. We just thought you might want to know."

"Thank you officer," Duane said, "please hold him until we get there, we are on our way right now."

When they arrived in Bend they took Gary aside and asked, "Why Gary? What did we do to make you want to run away from home?"

"Dad," he answered, "you and mom didn't do anything. But all my life I've listened to you and uncle Jerry talking about your adventures and I just wanted to have an adventure of my own."

Later my brother was telling me about it.

"What could I say, Jerry? I knew exactly where Gary was coming from so I just put my arm around him and said 'let's go home son!'

Duane died suddenly of a heart attack at age 46. To his dying day he insisted that, after eating those two huge meals in Williston, N. Dak. (Ron Benjamin and I eventually confessed about what happened) that I then went back to the freight yard and polished off the last half can of cold whole kernel corn.

Author's Note

It is not the intent of this book to promote or glamourize the smoking habit. I do not advocate the use of tobacco nor do I pass judgement on those who do. I myself gave up the habit many years ago and only the almighty can say for sure if the smoking habit had any bearing on Duane's fatal heart attack.